POWER IN NUMBERS

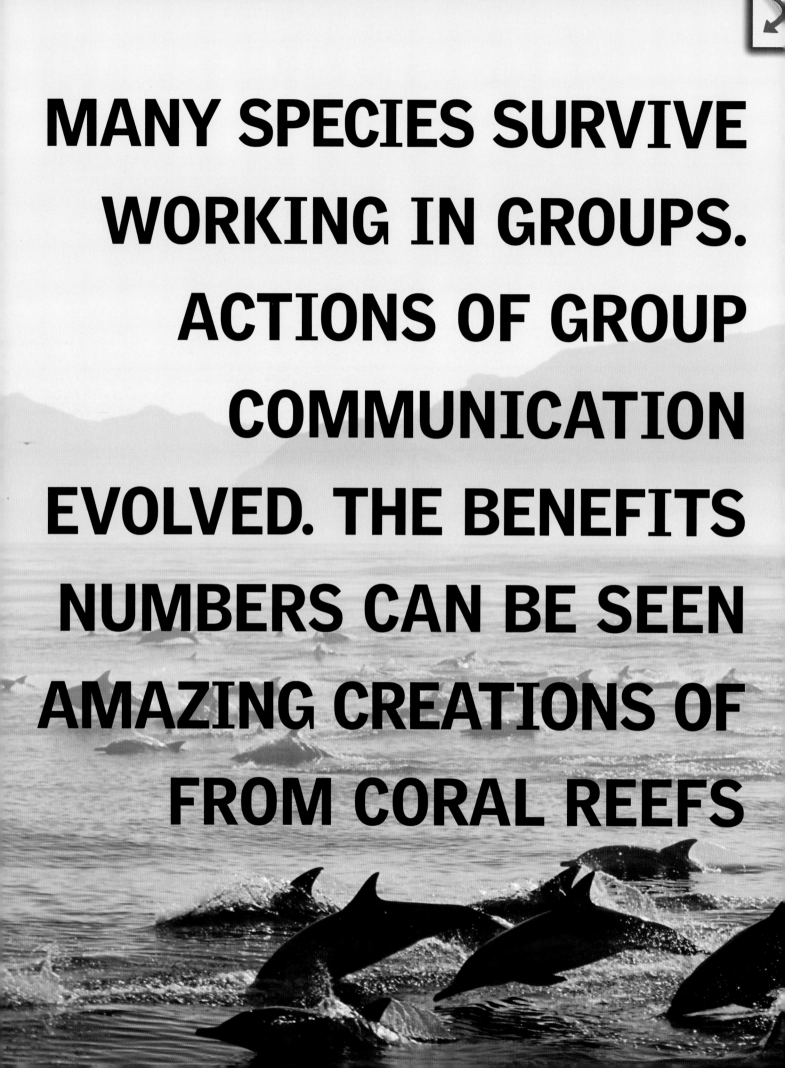

MANY SPECIES SURVIVE WORKING IN GROUPS. ACTIONS OF GROUP COMMUNICATION EVOLVED. THE BENEFITS NUMBERS CAN BE SEEN AMAZING CREATIONS OF FROM CORAL REEFS

BEST BY LIVING AND TO COORDINATE THE MEMBERS, COMPLEX SYSTEMS HAVE OF ACTING IN LARGE MOST VIVIDLY IN THE COLONIAL ORGANISMS, TO TERMITE MOUNDS.

POWER IN NUMBERS

1 ACTING TOGETHER

2 SAFETY IN NUMBERS

5 GROUP COMMUNICATION

6 PLANT GROUPS

3 MASS REPRODUCTION

4 COLONY LIFE

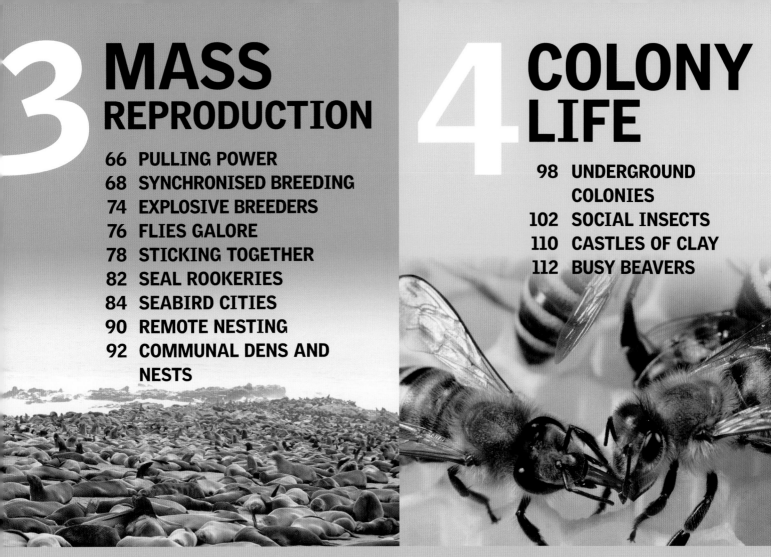

7 BOOM AND BUST

INTRODUCTION

FOR MANY SPECIES, CONGREGATING IN LARGE GROUPS BRINGS SIGNIFICANT ADVANTAGES. Some tasks can be achieved by teams or colonies of certain animals and plants that would be impossible for individuals acting on their own. For example, animals hunting in groups may be able to catch prey that would otherwise elude them. By working together, creatures can construct bigger, more complex living quarters. By cooperating, ants can get over insurmountable obstacles by building living 'bridges' with their own bodies.

When travelling together, schooling fish and migrating birds expend less energy by flying or swimming **in formation** rather than solo. Animals as diverse as emperor penguins, snakes and skunks survive the cold of winter by huddling together for warmth. In other cases, **division of labour** – with specific animals in a group taking different or specialised roles – provides increased efficiency in activities ranging from hunting to guarding their territory to caring for their young. The principle of **safety in numbers** means that an individual in a tightly knit group is less likely to be targeted by a predator than one subsisting on its own. Groups are also better at detecting, frightening away or confusing predators with tactics such as **alarm calls** and **mobbing behaviour**.

By **breeding en masse** and producing often huge amounts of **offspring**, many creatures ensure that at least some of the next generation will survive to carry on the group's genes. Similarly, by grouping together, plants synchronise blossoming times and produce copious amounts of pollen, to give themselves the best chance of achieving **pollination**.

The inherent power of numbers in the natural world is perhaps most forcefully expressed by **eusocial insects** – animals such as bees, wasps, ants and termites, which organise themselves into huge, industrious colonies that can persist for many times the lifespans of the individual members. In common with many other animal groups, these colonies are controlled by **complex messaging systems** to coordinate group activity and keep order.

There are also disadvantages to group living. For predators that hunt in groups, whatever prey they take has to be shared by the group, so weaker animals who cannot claim their share may sometimes be better off hunting smaller prey on their own. And for the hunted, groups of prey are more easily spotted by predators than single animals. Large colonies of animals are also susceptible to cycles of **population boom and bust** in response to such factors as disease, natural disasters, overcrowding or fluctuating predator numbers.

ACTING TOGETHER

1

OFF THE COAST OF ISLA SANTA CRUZ IN THE GALAPAGOS ISLANDS, a flight of blue-footed boobies plunge-dive into the ocean in pursuit of a shoal of herring. The resulting sound and commotion startle and confuse the fish, which more easily fall into the birds' eager beaks. This boisterous scene provides a classic example of how animals working in teams can succeed where individuals acting alone would not. Sometimes, as here, the result is achieved by sheer force of numbers, while in other cases the benefit derives from division of labour. Not just when hunting and feeding, but also when travelling together, animals can gain much through cooperation. Migrating birds and schooling fish expend less energy by flying or swimming in formation. On land, younger animals learn from more experienced travellers in the herd, troop or pack.

AMBUSH

SOME OF THE MOST IMPRESSIVE DISPLAYS OF ZOOLOGICAL TEAMWORK are performed by mammalian carnivores as they hunt down and kill their prey. Hunting tactics vary amongst these carnivores, but one of the most widespread methods is that of group ambush. Typically, this involves the hunters concealing themselves until the last possible moment, then launching a surprise attack on their prey, sometimes from several directions at once.

Masters of stealth

Lions, both African and Asiatic, are among the most accomplished exponents of group ambush. One reason for this is that lions are relatively slow-moving, compared to most of their potential prey. The maximum speed of an adult lion is around 55 km/h, while their favourite prey, zebras and wildebeest, can reach speeds of 70 km/h. Even the unwieldy African buffalo can sometimes outrun a lion. So in most instances, lions cannot rely on speed alone and must employ both stealth and teamwork to catch their prey. Cooperative hunting makes a big difference to their success

rates: a pride of lions hunting together is far more likely to make a kill than a pair of lions or a single lion working alone. Even so, lions succeed in only about 25 per cent of their attempts to capture medium-sized prey, such as zebras.

Within a pride, which can contain anything from 5 to 30 individuals, there are typically a small number of adult males (three at most) and a larger number of related lionesses, with the rest of the pride consisting of juveniles and cubs of both sexes. The lionesses do nearly all the hunting. Usually, there is a close correlation between prey size and the number of lionesses that participate in a hunt. No more than one or two lionesses are likely to be involved in hunting a small gazelle, three or four are needed to ambush a zebra or wildebeest, whereas to bring down a large buffalo all the adults in a pride, even the males, will usually participate.

Leonine hunts are well organised and often take place at night or in other conditions where the lions will not easily be spotted by their prey. The most common hunting tactic is the stealthy encirclement of a herd of prey animals, followed by the

WATCH AND WAIT A line of lionesses in Botswana's Okavango Delta stalk a herd of buffalo, aiming to encircle a suitable victim.

selection of a target – often an old or infirm animal, or a calf. Once the hunting group is as close as possible, they launch a series of short, powerful attacks in which individual lions run at and attempt to bring down the animal. Younger, faster lions will often run to outflank the prey, while slower, heavier ones go straight for it. In an alternative tactic, the younger lionesses in a pride may suddenly appear and startle a herd of prey animals, provoking them to run into a 'killing zone', where other more experienced lions are waiting to pounce. Sometimes one or more lions will wait in ambush at a water hole, jumping on unsuspecting animals when they arrive for a drink.

In most cases, a large prey animal, such as a buffalo, is brought down by a single lion jumping onto its back, using its claws to work towards the neck, and then delivering a powerful bite. Once the prey has been brought to the ground, several more lions will jump on or seize the victim's limbs to keep it pinned down. The final kill is often by suffocation or strangulation – a single lion will bite the victim's throat, crushing the windpipe, or clamp its mouth over the victim's nose and mouth.

Flushing out prey

Dholes, or Asiatic wild dogs, are also accomplished ambush predators. About the size of border collies, they are not fast runners, but through stealth and sheer numbers, they can overcome prey several times their body weight, such as deer and banteng (an ox of South-east Asia). A typical dhole hunting pack consists of six to nine animals, although sometimes several groups unite in order to hunt large animals. Their typical tactic is for one group to flush out prey from the bush, while others wait at the periphery to intercept the fleeing animals. Often when attacking a large animal, individual dholes will take particular roles in the hunt. For example, one will lead the chase, while another takes the first grab at the prey. Dholes will sometimes drive a deer into shallow water, then swim out and surround it before killing it.

RUNNING DOWN PREY

SOME OF THE MOST EFFICIENT PACK-HUNTERS IN THE WORLD ARE AFRICAN HUNTING DOGS, ALSO KNOWN AS CAPE HUNTING DOGS. These aggressive predators live in woodland–savannah areas rather than open grassy plains, with each pack occupying a home range of up to 1000 km^2. Their favoured prey include gazelles, impala and other antelopes, along with warthogs and wildebeest calves. They will also sometimes attack larger animals, such as adult wildebeest, zebra or ostriches, or take smaller mammals, such as rats.

The dogs rely primarily on stamina, gradually wearing down their prey over a protracted chase that can last for several kilometres. A hunt often commences with a rapid charge to stampede a herd of prey animals and identify a weak, sick or slow individual. The dogs have a top speed of up to 70 km/h, but during the chase in most hunts they

SUCCESSFUL CHASE African hunting dogs are in pursuit of an adult blue wildebeest in the Serengeti National Park, Tanzania. After an exhausting chase, the doomed animal finally succumbs to the pack (right).

average about 55 km/h, as they can maintain this speed for considerable distances. The dogs' long legs are particularly well adapted to long-distance running. Eventually, the prey animal is too exhausted to continue, and turns to confront its attackers – usually with rapidly fatal results.

Close cooperation between the members of the hunting pack – typically consisting of six to ten dogs led by the alpha male – is a key factor in the chase: in a strictly observed rota, each dog takes it in turn to move in and harass the prey animal. Nearly 80 per cent of all hunts executed by the dogs end in a kill, which is usually quick – one dog will seize the prey's tail in its jaws, a second goes for the lips, and the remainder rip out the unfortunate animal's innards while it is unable to move. Although this method might seem brutal, in fact it kills large prey more quickly than the strangulation techniques adopted by big cats. After a successful hunt and feeding session, the returning dogs

will regurgitate meat for the pups and nursing females that remained at the den. They also feed other pack members that cannot keep up, such as the sick, injured or old.

Keeping in touch

To improve the efficiency of their hunts, African hunting dogs utilise a variety of techniques for communicating with each other. Each dog has a distinctive black, white and fawn pattern to its coat and a bushy tail with a noticeably white tip: these features may help each member of a hunting team to keep track of the others' positions during the chase. Members of a pack also vocalise to help coordinate their movements. Calls range from rallying howls to squeaking and chirping sounds. The dogs have a particular ceremony that initiates each hunt: they circulate among themselves, brushing against each other and vocalising until excited. The importance of sound as a means of communication is apparent from the size of the dogs' ears.

There were once about 500 000 African hunting dogs across 39 countries, with packs of 100 or more not uncommon. Now there are only about 5000 dogs in 25 countries, with the main concentrations in Tanzania, northern Botswana and eastern Namibia. Part of the reason for this dramatic decline is due to the hunting efficiency of different sizes of pack. It seems that the optimum size is around 15 to 20 dogs. Once numbers decline below this, due to factors such as habitat loss, hunting forays tend to be less successful and adults may be unable to provide enough food for their pups. And with fewer pups surviving to adulthood, pack sizes then decrease even further.

Cheetahs as group hunters

Africa's savannah is home to the world's fastest sprinter, the cheetah, which over short distances can exceed speeds of 96 km/h. Cheetahs are usually solitary hunters, but there are occasions when they will also hunt cooperatively, by chasing down their prey.

Young cheetahs sometimes hunt with their mothers. When they become adults, groups of two or three males, called coalitions – often (though not always) brothers – will sometimes continue group hunting for many years. The success rates of these hunting groups are thought to be somewhat higher than when individuals hunt alone, although it is unclear whether this converts into a real benefit to the individual cheetahs, because the food from the kill will have to be shared between members of the coalition. Where group hunting is almost certainly beneficial is that it allows the cheetahs to defend larger territories more easily, giving readier access to prey animals and to female cheetahs that stray into these territories.

Jackal families

The black-backed jackal, another inhabitant of African savannah and woodland, tends to hunt alone or in pairs, but when food is scarce the extended family, including juveniles, may hunt together by chasing down prey. One jackal pursues the prey, such as a new-born antelope, while

YOUNG CHASERS Juvenile cheetahs in the Masai Mara Game Reserve in Kenya learn to chase prey under the guidance of their mother. Here they have encircled a baby impala.

the others cut off its escape. Some of the jackals transport meat back to their dens in their stomach, to reduce the risk of one of their main competitors – spotted hyenas – stealing it. The food is then regurgitated for the pups.

FACTS

THE HARRIS HAWK IS THE only bird of prey to hunt cooperatively in a group, called a cast, typically consisting of three to six birds. By hunting together, they can successfully flush out and pursue quarry such as rabbits.

WOLVES RUN DOWN PREY. Each hunt involves complex communication before, during and after the kill. A single wolf can eat up to 3.5 kg of food at a time.

CHIMPANZEES are known to hunt red colobus monkeys cooperatively, using ambush tactics. While one group chases the monkeys through the forest canopy, another races forward to head them off.

SPOTTED HYENA

USING THEIR EXTRAORDINARY STAMINA TO

WEAR DOWN THEIR PREY, AFRICA'S SPOTTED HYENAS KILL MORE GAZELLES
and wildebeest than lions and cheetahs put together. Also known as laughing hyenas for their high-pitched bark, they live in groups called clans and hunt mainly at night, sometimes alone but most successfully in groups. During a group hunt, the animals approach prey from downwind in fan formation, dispersing herds of prey animals until they spot one that is lame or young. After a chase of one or two kilometres, the target animal inevitably flags, while the hyenas are still going strong.

Once the pursuers have seized and killed their victim, they begin to show their remarkable anatomical strength. The jaws of a spotted hyena are unbelievably powerful and their specialised teeth are designed to crack open the largest of bones. But the organ that sets them above all other African hunters is their stomach. Spotted hyena stomachs contain hydrochloric acid in such concentrated form that it can dissolve large chunks of bone, an adaptation that enables hyenas to eat practically all of their kill. And they are fast eaters: a clan of 10 to 12 can demolish a wildebeest in just 15 minutes.

VITAL STATISTICS

CLASS: Mammalia
ORDER: Carnivora
SPECIES: *Crocuta crocuta*
HABITAT: Grassland savannah
DISTRIBUTION: Sub-Saharan Africa
KEY FEATURES: Immense stamina, exceptionally strong jaws and teeth, and a stomach that can digest bone

FISHING GANGS

IN THE ANIMAL WORLD, FISHING IS OFTEN PERFORMED MOST EFFICIENTLY AS A GROUP HUNT, particularly when the fish prey are themselves in a large group, called a school or shoal. Several members of the bird order Pelecaniformes – including pelicans, cormorants, shags and other bird groups, such as frigate birds – frequently gather in large numbers to fish. In southern Europe, Asia and Africa, great white pelicans, which have a wingspan of nearly 3 m and are one of the world's largest flying birds, collect in groups of up to 500. They form lines to herd schools of small fish into shallow water, then simply scoop them up into their net-like bills. Large fish are snatched first with the bill-tip, then tossed up in the air to be caught on the way down, sliding headfirst into the bird's gullet.

In the Southern Ocean, blue-eyed shags often form dense 'rafts' at sea of up to 2000 birds. The birds, which are characterised by a vivid-blue ring around their eyes and an orange–yellow growth on their beaks, herd fish into shallower water and then

HEADS DOWN Great white pelicans arrayed in feeding formation around the edge of Kenya's Lake Nakuru.

SHARK PATROL On a reef at Bikini Atoll in the western Pacific, a group of grey reef sharks scout around the coral heads in search of a satisfying meal.

break rank, diving down to catch them. By fishing in such large groups they help each other by panicking the fish into having nowhere to go except into the beak of the next bird. Shags are excellent divers with a recorded maximum dive of 130 m. Similar behaviour has been observed among double-crested cormorants off the coasts of North America.

Plunge-divers

All species of gannets and boobies (related groups of seabird that are also members of the order Pelecaniformes) catch fish and squid by plunge-diving from height into the sea and then pursuing their prey underwater. But one species in particular, the blue-footed booby, so-called for its distinctive bright-blue feet, has refined the technique of plunge-diving into spectacular group displays. When hunting for fish and squid, the boobies will fly in groups of 10, 20, even 50 birds at a height of around 15–20 m – often quite near to shore – with their bills pointing downwards. When they spot a shoal of fish near the sea surface, they check their flight, the lead bird signals to the rest of the group and they dive in unison, folding their wings just before entry into the water. With a torpedo-shaped body, tapered bill and pointed tail, the blue-footed booby is well-adapted for penetrating water, while air sacs in the skull cushion the impact of the dive.

Underwater, momentum takes the boobies down to a depth of about 3 m, where they swim for a second or two, attempting to catch fish in their bills, before bobbing to the surface. Sometimes, to achieve greater depth, the plunge-diving is performed from even greater heights of up to 30 m. The synchronised diving is thought to confuse and startle the individual fish in target shoals, helping to temporarily immobilise them so that they are more easily caught.

Shark squadrons

Although there is a popular conception that sharks are 'lone killers', many shark species feed cooperatively in groups. Large schools of grey reef sharks gather around the edges of coral reefs in order to intercept fish coming up from the depths. On reef surfaces, squadrons of

whitetip sharks have been observed herding huge schools of snapper, or poking their wedge-shaped heads into cracks and crevices. If one shark locates prey, the rest pile in. The result is a squirming mass of sharks.

Sand tiger sharks have also occasionally been reported feeding cooperatively. On the coast of New South Wales, scuba divers observed a pack of sand tigers herding a small shoal of juvenile yellowtail kingfish. The sharks accomplished this by whipping their tails to generate sharp underwater pressure waves. Similarly, off North Carolina, a group of 100 or more sand tigers has been observed concentrating and capturing a school of bluefish. The sharks systematically surrounded the bluefish and herded them into shallow water, then suddenly dashed in to attack their nearly stranded prey.

This illustrates quite advanced cooperative behaviour. When faced with a hunting predator, schooling fish tend to crowd together instinctively, but unless they are skilfully contained, they are adept at slipping out and escaping through gaps. Yet however agile they are in their liquid element, fish tend to become quite helpless when confined in shallow water – hence the sand tigers' success in first containing, and then subduing, their prey.

The sand tiger sharks surrounded the bluefish and herded them into shallow water, then suddenly dashed in to attack their nearly stranded prey.

DOLPHIN DAYS

DOLPHINS ARE UNDOUBTEDLY THE MOST IMPRESSIVE COOPERATIVE HUNTERS IN THE SEA. White-beaked dolphins, for example, which live in the cool waters of the North Atlantic, employ complex teamwork to herd and entrap their prey. By working together, they reduce the amount of energy expended by any one individual. One technique involves a small group of dolphins congregating beneath a shoal of fish and then charging

DRIVEN AGROUND A pod of bottlenose dolphins has managed to strand some mullet on a mudflat in South Carolina.

upwards, while other dolphins converge on the fish at the surface. The effect is to cause the fish first to group together into a tight 'ball', then to scatter suddenly, allowing the dolphins to pick them off individually. Herding fish in this way is highly cooperative, requiring precise synchronisation of the dolphin dives, surface rushes and re-grouping. During these exercises, the dolphins communicate with others in their pod by using whistles and performing tail slaps and somersaults.

Before dolphins can feed, they first have to find sizeable schools of fish. Because these schools tend to move around continuously, the dolphins must search for their prey. If they remain in just one small area, they soon exhaust the available food supply. Therefore, they tend to leave and revisit feeding grounds on a periodic basis. By acting cooperatively, they can cover a wider area and combine their collective experience.

To locate fish schools, dolphins mainly use echolocation, often in a highly organised manner. Off the coast of Argentina, for example, dusky dolphins spend most of their time resting in small groups near to shore, but in the afternoon they go hunting. To locate schools of anchovy, several dolphins swim side by side, spread out in line abreast. This allows them to scan the widest possible area of the sea ahead.

Common dolphins hunt together in the Sea of Cortez (the Gulf of California) in groups numbering up to a thousand or more. To maximise their chances of finding large fish schools, they pay attention to seasonal changes in wind direction. In an oceanographic phenomenon called Ekman transport, the predominantly northerly winds of winter move water away from the coast on the eastern side of the Gulf. This causes upwelling that drags nutrients up from the seabed, encouraging the growth

of plankton, which in turn attracts fish. When the winds change to southerly, the upwelling occurs on the western side of the Gulf. So the dolphins concentrate their activity in the east during winter, switching to the west in summer.

Various species of dolphin that frequently live and hunt around coasts, such as bottlenose dolphins, often make use of coastal topography in their fish-herding activities. For example, they have been seen herding fish against structures such as marina walls, and then taking it in turns to feed. Bottlenose dolphins have also been known to chase prey such as mullet into very shallow water, trapping schools of fish against sandbars. They may even lunge onto mudflats in pursuit of stranded, panicked fish, almost beaching themselves in the process.

Open-sea techniques

In the open ocean, several dolphin species use the surface of the water as a barrier against which to herd schools of fish. To do this effectively requires a fairly large number of dolphins – 10 or more – to circle continuously around and underneath the school of fish, gradually nudging it upwards. Once the fish have been forced near the surface, seabirds soon arrive to take advantage, and the resulting commotion often attracts the attention of more dolphins, which eases the herding task. Groups of up to 300 dolphins have been observed fishing together.

Once the fish have been corralled into a reasonably tight ball, the dolphins take turns to charge through the school to feed. Scientists have theorised that some dolphins may use a burst pulse – a stream of very powerful sounds – to stun or confuse prey before snapping them up. Bottlenose dolphins also sometimes use a fish-corralling technique known as pinwheeling, in which they rapidly spin around an individual fish, encircling it to cut off its escape. Orcas, the largest of all dolphins, have been observed circling herring with vigorous splashing and noise-making displays in order to corral the fish.

Cooperating with humans

Dolphins not only cooperate with their own kind to track down and catch prey, some species will also cooperate with humans. On the west coast of Africa, bottlenose dolphins herd mullet to the shallows where native fishermen wait with gill nets to trap the fish. The fishermen allow the dolphins to eat their fill, then take the rest. The fishermen can apparently alert the dolphins to feeding time by slapping the water with sticks.

Similarly in the coastal town of Laguna, in southern Brazil, a pod of bottlenose dolphins alerts the local fishermen to 'feeding time' by stationing themselves offshore in a line. When some of the dolphins leave the line, swim seawards and return, the men wait close to shore with their nets. When the dolphins reappear and dive just out of net range, the fishermen cast their nets, shortly to find them brimming with fish. The dolphins take advantage of the resulting confusion in the water and feed on escaping fish. This collaboration has been known about for decades, and there are also historical accounts of dolphins cooperatively fishing with Australian Aborigines.

COOPERATIVE WHALE FISHING

TAKING THE BAIT A minke whale surfaces at speed after lunging though a bait ball under seagulls off the north coast of Iceland. Like all baleen whales, minkes are seasonal feeders.

LIKE OTHER BALEEN WHALES, HUMPBACK WHALES USE THEIR LARGE BALEEN PLATES TO FILTER HUGE MOUTHFULS OF FOOD FROM THE OCEAN. They are seasonal feeders, migrating to rich polar waters each summer to feed. Humpbacks then swim to warm tropical or sub-tropical waters in winter to breed and calve, living off the fat reserves that they built up in summer. While for most of the year the humpback whales avoid others of their kind – the males are particularly aggressive to one another – on their feeding grounds they hunt cooperatively, performing complex fishing techniques.

Most commonly, a group of whales pushes through shoals of krill or herring in echelon formation – each whale positioned stepwise to the rear and slightly to the left or right of the whale ahead to form an oblique or V-shaped line-up. This has the advantage that most of the fish or krill that escape the jaws of the lead whale are swept into the mouth of the next animal in line, to left or right.

Bubble-net feeding

The most unusual and spectacular of the humpback whale's fishing methods is bubble-net feeding (also called lunge feeding), which is used to round up highly concentrated masses of prey. The technique is unique to humpback whales, but it is not practised by all members

of the species and has been observed in only a few locations, notably off the coasts of south-eastern Alaska and north-eastern Canada, and off the Pacific coast of South America.

A small number of whales – typically five to eight – always make up the same fishing party, with each whale having its own place and role in the team. First the whales dive beneath a shoal of herring, other small fish or mass of krill, to a depth of some 15–20 m. One humpback then slowly begins to move upwards in a clockwise spiral path, about 20 m across, exhaling air through its blowholes as it does so. This creates a dense, cylindrical wall of bubbles or 'bubble-net' through which the fish or krill will not pass, thus trapping themselves inside.

Other members of the hunting team then begin moving upwards within the cylinder, some of them vocalising bellows or screams to scare or confuse the fish and help to concentrate them near the surface, where they form a giant mass of food. The entire team of whales then rises to the surface as one, like a giant flower opening on the surface of the sea, with their mouths agape to capture their large meal. As the whales open their gigantic mouths, their jaws are able to 'unhinge' and extend to create an even larger volume for consuming the fish or krill. With nowhere left to go, the prey jump wildly, but

> **One humpback slowly begins to move upwards in a clockwise spiral path, about 20m across, exhaling air through its blowholes as it does so. This creates a dense cylindrical wall of bubbles or 'bubble-net' through which the fish or krill will not pass.**

the huge whale mouths are waiting to scoop them up. Any prey that manages to leap out of the mouth of one humpback usually ends up in the mouth of another. Sometimes huge rafts of long-tailed ducks, together with other opportunistic scavengers, such as Steller sea lions, gulls and shearwaters, will crowd around the whales to 'cash in' on the food bounty.

Bowhead, minke and sperm whales

Compared to humpback whales, other species of baleen whale are generally less inclined to engage in cooperative hunting. A baleen species that spends its entire life in Arctic waters, the bowhead or Greenland right whale, has occasionally been observed feeding in groups of up to five individuals. They move through the water either in line abreast or in V-shaped or oblique echelon formation, separated from each other by a distance of 10–50 m, and skim the sea surface for krill, sea butterflies and

BUBBLE-NET FEEDING Several adult humpback whales gorge themselves at the sea surface off the south-eastern coast of Alaska.

copepods. In Scotland's Moray Firth, minke whales (another baleen species) do not corral fish like humpbacks but rely on other sea creatures to do the corralling for them. The minkes watch for dense rafts of seabirds, such as kittiwakes, herring gulls, guillemots and shearwaters, to know where to fish. The birds are there because shoals of mackerel concentrate sand eels into tight bait balls that they push towards the surface. The birds feed on the sand eels and so do the whales.

Among the toothed whales, sperm whales are known to coordinate foraging dives down to depths of several hundred, sometimes a few thousand, metres. During these dives, the whale group is locating, catching and swallowing squid. At the end of a dive, which can last for up to 40 minutes, the group returns to the surface in a coordinated manner. Sonar studies have shown that the foraging whales sometimes spread out in an underwater line up to 500 m in length. Most sperm whales live in pods consisting of several adult females and their calves, and because all members of a pod take part in protecting young whales (who cannot dive deeply), females who have recently calved are not precluded from joining the deep-dive squid hunts.

COMPLEX

AMONG THE MULTITUDINOUS INHABITANTS OF THE MARINE ENVIRONMENT, many that look like single plants or animals are in fact complex colonies of tiny animals that are permanently joined together. Although each animal in the colony is an individual, the integration of the whole group is so strong – they live, act and feed together – that the colony attains the character of a single, large individual, a 'super-organism'. The majority of these superorganisms belong to a handful of invertebrate animal groups, notably the cnidarians, tunicates and bryozoans.

Cnidarians comprise a huge phylum (major division) of aquatic animals in which the body form of each individual animal is based either on a tube-like structure called a polyp, or a bell-shaped structure called a medusa. Members of two particular cnidarian groups – hydrozoans and corals – form a variety of superorganisms. Tunicates, which include sea squirts and salps, are sac-like filterfeeders, some of which also form into large colonies. Bryozoans, or sea mats, are almost invariably colonial and form encrustations on objects such as submerged rocks and seaweeds.

Creature of many parts – the Portuguese man-of-war

The hydrozoans are a large and diverse group of cnidarians, with many different body shapes and lifestyles. Most exist in colonies consisting of tens to thousands of polyps, a classic example being the Portuguese man-of-war. Belonging to a group of free-floating hydrozoans called the siphonophores, this is a complex colony of hundreds of individual polypoid (polyp-shaped) animals called zooids. These fall into four different types, each dependent on the others for survival, with a well-defined division of labour.

The uppermost part of a Portuguese man-of-war, poking above the sea surface, is a gas-filled structure called the float bladder, which consists of a single individual

DEADLY WEAPON Stings from the tentacles of a Portuguese man-of-war are excruciatingly painful to humans and can even be fatal.

GREY MATTER One of many types of reef-building hard coral, a brain coral consists of thousands of polyps arranged in sinuous rows, resembling the folds of a human brain.

SEA COLONIES

polyp. This bottle or pear-shaped sac, which can exceed 15 cm in length, provides buoyancy for the rest of the colony and acts as a sail. Beneath the float are long tentacles, up to several metres in length. These are made up of polyps called dactylozooids, which are concerned with the detection and capture of food. Associated with these are digestive polyps, called gastrozooids. These are the colony's 'stomachs' and respond quickly to the presence of food. Each resting gastrozooid measures only 1–2 mm in diameter but its mouth may expand to more than 2 cm as it fastens onto and spreads over a morsel of food, which it then digests by secreting enzymes that break the food down into simple nutrients. The fourth class of polyp, the gonozooids, are concerned with reproduction.

As a Portuguese man-of-war is pushed along by the wind, its long tentacles fish continuously through the water. As they come into contact with small fish, shrimp and other surface plankton, the dactylozooids deploy their stinging capsules to paralyse the prey. Muscles in the tentacles then contract and drag the food into the range of the gastrozooids, which attach to the immobilised victim and, acting like small mouths, digest it.

Carnivorous corals

The corals belong to a group of cnidarians called the anthozoans, which also include sea anemones. Most corals consist of colonies of thousands to tens of thousands of individual polyps, which are all anatomically identical and function in the same way. With their bright colours, waving tentacles and, in some cases, fleshy trunks, many coral colonies look like plants but, as with all cnidarians, they are actually voracious carnivores.

Each coral polyp is usually just a few millimetres wide and has a fleshy sac-like structure with a stomach at the centre and an upper opening, the mouth, through which it takes in food. Surrounding the mouth are numerous tentacles, armed with nematocysts (stinging capsules), which catch prey. Internally, an important contributor to the life of many corals is the presence within the polyps of tiny algal organisms called zooxanthellae. These provide energy-containing nutrients that are then used by the polyps. The algae can thrive without the danger of being eaten, and they make use of the waste products of the coral. The corals, in turn, use the excess sugars and other substances produced by the algae as a source of food.

Corals fall into two main types: stony (or hard) and soft corals. The polyps of stony corals secrete a hard substance, calcium carbonate. As the colony grows, this gradually builds up into a skeleton, which acts as a substrate on which the living coral polyps can thrive and multiply. The skeleton of each coral

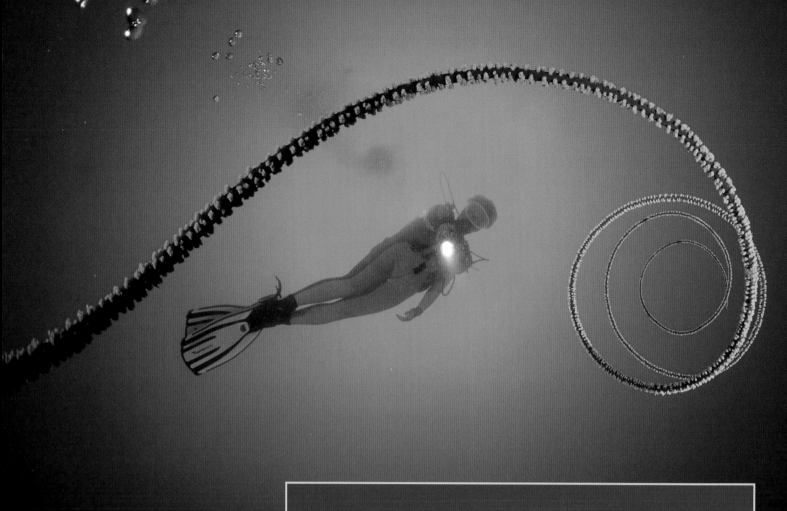

WIRE CORAL A scuba diver observes a wire coral, a type of soft coral, in the Indian Ocean. A close-up view (right) reveals the individual polyps, with a tiny shrimp straddling several of them.

species takes up a shape that is characteristic of that species. Different varieties of stony coral include staghorn, finger, brain, pillar, star, plate, lettuce and golfball corals – names that reflect the shapes of the skeletons laid down by the different colonies. Over time, the skeletons of stony corals provide the main building materials of the structures called coral reefs.

Soft corals, or alcyonarians, do not produce calcium carbonate and so do not contribute significantly to reef building. They have flexible skeletons containing minute, spiny elements called sclerites. Varieties of soft coral include sea fans, sea whips, sea pens, dead-man's fingers and wire corals.

It was once assumed that the individual polyps in a coral colony act independently, catching and digesting their food in an uncoordinated fashion. In fact, it is now known that there is some sharing of nutrients between the polyps – nutrients can move through a colony by means of a system of canals ranging in size up to half a millimetre in diameter.

Sea squirts, salps and pyrosomes

Tunicates are a group of marine animals that obtain their nutrition by drawing seawater through their bodies and filtering out particles of food, which are then digested within an internal gut. The archetypal tunicates are animals known as sea squirts, which live fastened to objects on the sea bottom, such as rocks. Each individual consists of a sac enclosed by a flexible outer covering called the 'tunic'. Through an opening in the tunic, called the inhalant siphon, a sea squirt can draw seawater into its sac. Later it expels this water, together with waste matter, through another opening, the exhalant siphon. Many sea squirts are colonial, consisting of hundreds or thousands of individual animals, called zooids, joined together to form a superorganism. The zooids in these colonies often have their own separate inhalant siphons but a shared exhalant siphon. The size of the zooids varies enormously, from a millimetre to several centimetres across. Likewise the colonies vary greatly, from a few centimetres to several metres wide. A typical example of a colonial sea squirt is the star sea squirt. Individuals of this species are only 2 mm long and cannot live on their own. Instead, they collect in star-shaped clusters, which are embedded in a shared gelatinous casing.

Other than sea squirts, two types of colony-forming tunicate float freely in the ocean: salps and pyrosomes. Salps move around by jet propulsion, taking in water at one end of their bodies and expelling it from the other. They frequently group together in colonies that take the form of clumps or chains of animals stacked side by side, which can be up to a metre long. Pyrosomes are composed of thousands of individual zooids, joined together to form a hollow cylinder, which is closed at one end and open at the other, like a giant planktonic test tube.

Some pyrosomes reach enormous proportions – the largest ever seen, in the sea off New Zealand, was over 20 m long and its body wide enough for a scuba diver to swim inside. An additional remarkable quality of pyrosomes is that they are bioluminescent – each of its zooids bears two organs containing light-manufacturing bacteria, so that if lightly stroked, waves of blue-green chemical light pass over the colony's exterior. It is probable that this bioluminescent ability is a defence to frighten off predators. When a pyrosome is touched, the disturbed zooids stop taking in water and turn on their lights. This signals neighbouring individuals to do the same. As a result, the colony stops moving and a ripple of dazzling light sweeps down it.

Sea mats

Sea mats, or bryozoans, are colonies made up of numerous tiny zooids that build little box-shaped cases around themselves, made of either calcium carbonate or a gelatinous or horny material. Small holes between the cases interconnect the individual zooids, which can number up to several million per colony. To feed, a zooid pushes a circular or horseshoe-shaped structure, a lophophore, out of an opening in its case. This is crowned by tentacles covered in tiny hairs that trap and draw in food particles.

Bryozoan colonies can be anything up to several metres in size and often have a mat-like form, encrusting the surface of stones and seaweeds. Some colonies develop into branching plant or fungus-like shapes. In each colony, different zooids assume different functions. Some gather up food, others are devoted to strengthening it, others to deterring predators, and still others have reproductive functions or are charged with cleaning the colony. A few bryozoans can move slowly through sand by

FLUTED BRYOZOAN This sea mat (bryozoan) found on the sea floor off California actually comprises tens of thousands of individual animals (top).

JET-PROPELLED SALP A spherical clump of transparent organisms floats near the surface of the Red Sea (bottom).

coordinated rowing movements of long projections found on specialised zooids. In short, bryozoans comprise some of the most diverse and remarkable superorganisms on the planet.

Algal colonies

Some types of green algae, or chlorophytes, which belong to the plant kingdom, also form colonies that can be thought of as superorganisms. Volvox, for example, is the most developed in a group of chlorophytes that form spherical colonies. Each volvox colony is composed of several hundred interconnected algal cells, each an individual organism, bearing two flagella, or whip-like hairs, which can be used to propel the whole colony around. These cells also have small, red, light-detecting eye-spots, which are more developed in the algal cells on one side of the colony than on the other – in other words, the whole colony has distinct back and front ends. This differentiation between the cells on the two sides enables the colony to detect and swim towards light.

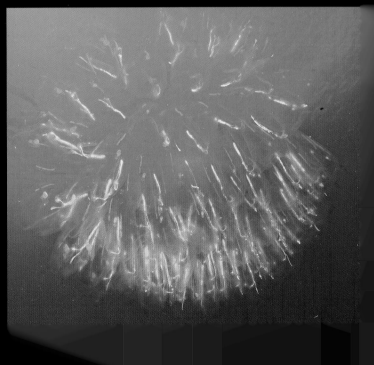

ELEPHANT JOURNEYS

IN THE REGION SOUTH OF TIMBUKTU, WHERE THE SAND DUNES OF THE SAHARA GIVE WAY TO A SCATTERING OF SHRUBS AND TREES, live the world's most well-travelled elephants – Mali's desert elephants. Numbering a few hundred individuals, they migrate almost 500 km in a year, and sometimes as much as 50 km in a single day, in pursuit of food and water.

Scientific tracking of the elephants has revealed that they follow a vast trek each year around southern Mali, sometimes straying further south into neighbouring Burkina Faso. The trek follows a roughly circular, anti-clockwise route dotted with temporary and permanent watering holes. During the heat of the day, when air temperatures routinely reach 35°C, the elephants rest under clumps of thorny acacia, emerging to drink from waterholes and to continue their journey only in the evening, early morning and sometimes the cool of the night. The desert elephants have somewhat smaller bodies, larger feet and longer legs than their relatives on the savannah – adaptations to the dry and sandy conditions and the epic distances that they cover.

Some 3000 km to the south-east of Mali, in a north-western section of the Namib Desert, lives a second population of desert elephants, several thousand strong. Each year,

JUNGLE JOURNEY Forest elephants trample their way through vegetation in Rwanda's Parc National des Volcans.

LONG TREK A group of elephants in Damaraland, Namibia, follows a dry riverbed that forms one of their habitual routes between watering holes.

groups of these elephants make marathon treks between the shores of Namibia's Skeleton Coast and the high mountains of the interior in the search for water – of which they need to drink around 100 litres a day. They mainly follow dry riverbeds and although for much of the time there is no water on the surface, it is sometimes present beneath the ground. The elephants are well aware of this and occasionally stop to dig for water.

The desert elephants, like most elephants, undertake their migrations in herds, most commonly in a family unit of about 3 to 10 adult females and their young. Adult males are excluded from these units and generally travel in smaller, all-male groups of the same age. Within the family units, there is always a leader, the matriarch, who is the grandmother or great-grandmother of her group – most of the other females in the herd will be her daughters or granddaughters, although sometimes one of the matriarch's sisters and her offspring will also be present. The matriarch is the one who decides the route and shows other herd members the water sources she knows, which the rest memorise.

To get quickly through areas that are potentially dangerous due to scarcity of water or the presence of lions, who will occasionally attack juvenile elephants, the herds will sometimes 'streak' along well-worn corridors, usually at night. On every journey, one of the largest adult elephants is positioned at the front of the herd and another at the rear. If danger threatens, the group takes up defensive formation, with young elephants protected by the matriarch and other large females.

During migrations, there is some evidence that individual elephant herds may form units within larger travelling supergroups. Although separated spatially by 10 km or more, these herds can communicate with each other in various ways, including the use of bellowing calls and vibrations transmitted through the ground, which can be detected by special receptors in the elephants' toes, heels and trunks.

Forest elephants

The African forest elephant has recently been recognised as a separate species from the African bush elephant (of which desert elephants are a subgroup). Like desert elephants, they are smaller than the savannah elephants, and they also undertake long annual migrations in family groups, directing these treks along well-trodden jungle corridors in search of particular species of fruiting trees.

EVERY SPRING AND AUTUMN ON THE WESTERN STEPPE OF KAZAKHSTAN, A REMARKABLE SIGHT UNFOLDS, as tens of thousands of saiga antelope stream across the landscape. The saiga are making the journey between their semi-desert wintering grounds to the south and the richer grazing pastures to the north, where they pass their summers.

Like other antelopes, the saiga live in huge herds as a defence against predation. They spend the bulk of their time grazing, which makes them easy targets for predators, including wolves and eagles. In a large herd, the chances are higher that some of the animals will sense the approach of an attacker and alert the others before the predator strikes.

As with most ungulate (hoofed animal) migrations, the saiga undertake their journeys primarily because of rain or the lack of it. When a seasonal drought dries up grass and water supplies in one area along the migration route, the animals move on to the next area where rains are falling. These mass movements can take their toll – sometimes thousands perish in extreme weather. But migration is a way of life for the saiga. So with their heads

MIGRATING HERDS

lowered to the ground they march or canter across the steppe for hours on end, sometimes producing a remarkable turn of speed when required. Large air sacs in the saiga's proboscis-like nose help to pre-warm cold air as it is breathed in and also extract valuable moisture from exhaled air. The long nose is also designed to filter out the dust that is churned up as the animals cross the steppe. The brownish fur turns whiter and much thicker in winter – another adaptation to the harsh conditions.

Much larger migrating herds of saiga – up to a million animals in some cases – once roamed across the Asian steppes and their range extended all the way from northern Europe to China. Today, their numbers are much reduced, largely as a result

SAIGA MIGRATION Saiga females give birth to their offspring (inset, left) in May, before joining in the procession across the steppe of Kazakhstan. Sometimes marching, sometimes running, herds can cover up to 120 km per day.

of poaching of the male antelopes for their horns (these are prized in China for their use in traditional medicine). The male saigas already have a pressurised existence. During the rutting season, between late November and late December, they must defend their breeding territories against other males in fierce fights that quite frequently end in the death of one of the combatants. So much energy is spent in this defence of territories that during the extremely cold steppe winters up to 97 per cent of the sexually mature saiga males perish.

The males that survive begin their spring migration at the end of April, forming relatively small herds. It is the female saiga that congregate more noticeably as they move towards their breeding grounds, where they give birth to one or two calves each. A week or so later, mothers and offspring join together in the very largest herds, following the males on treks that may go on for several hundred kilometres. Once the migration has finished, the streams of animals break up and disperse into smaller groups of 30–40 animals.

SUPERGROUPS

THE EURASIAN SAIGA ANTELOPE IS NOT THE ONLY CONGREGATIONAL SPECIES THAT ONCE FORMED MUCH LARGER MIGRATING HERDS THAN THOSE SEEN TODAY. Until the mid-19th century groups of bison containing tens of millions of individual animals roamed the great plains of North America, while in South Africa migrating herds of springbok could reach an incredible 150 km long. Although herds of this magnitude may never be seen on Earth again, there are some regions in the world where highly impressive migratory spectacles can still be witnessed.

In East Africa, nearly 2 million ungulates undertake an annual migration that begins and ends in the southern part of the Serengeti grasslands, dictated by seasonal rains and periods of drought. Over a period of eight months, the gigantic assemblage of wildlife sweeps up into south-western Kenya and then, after a pause, returns south again, following a roughly circular, clockwise route, which totals over 1000 km.

The Serengeti migration originates from the seemingly unending open plains of the Serengeti National Park and the Ngorongoro Conservation Area of northern Tanzania. From December until March, these grasslands are inhabited by enormous herds of wildebeest, zebra, gazelles and other ungulates, which graze on grass recently ripened by the 'short rains' that occur between October and early December. The period between late January and March is the main calving season for these herds, and they attract large numbers of predators such as lions, hyenas and cheetahs. At this time, the wildebeest herds are at their most structured, with groupings of pregnant females, collections of other females that have calved with their offspring, and small bands of yearlings and bachelor herds.

The southern Serengeti grasslands are rich in the minerals necessary for lactation, but lack water for most of the year. As the 'long rains' diminish by the end of April, water reserves become depleted and unable to sustain the vast herds. The dry season looms and the huge population of animals starts massing for the long trek north.

The herds sweep first in a north-westerly direction, moving to the long grass plains and woodland of the Serengeti's Western Corridor, almost to Lake Victoria. By the end of May they have exhausted the best pastures in this region and begin to move in a northeasterly direction, heading for the short sweet grasses and woodlands of the Masai Mara Game Reserve of south-western Kenya. Arriving there in July and August, they remain on the productive Mara grasslands for three or four months, the Mara River and its tributaries providing the herds with water during this dry period. Then, as the storm clouds gather in the south, they begin their return journey towards the now green pastures of the southern Serengeti. During the calving season, the herds rest and partially disperse. But come late March, they begin to reassemble, and the whole cycle of migration starts again.

By far the most numerous participants in this migration are blue wildebeest, which number up to 1.4 million individuals, but they do not travel alone. Also present are some 300 000 Thomson's gazelle (a small horned antelope), which typically precede the wildebeest herds, and 200 000 plains zebra, which either mingle with the wildebeest or follow on behind. About 12 000 common eland (a large horned antelope) also take part. The plains zebra are particularly beneficial travelling companions for the wildebeest, since they quickly consume the longer grasses in highly vegetated areas, exposing the more nutritional short grasses, which the wildebeest prefer.

Many of the migrating ungulates die from exhaustion or are picked off by predators during the gigantic annual trek. The most perilous passages are the crossings of the swollen Mara River, which lies across the path of both the northerly and southerly migration routes. Usually, the crossing places chosen by the lead animals in a group are shallow, with easily negotiated river embankments, and the majority of the migrants pass safely across. But the leaders can get it wrong. If the riverbanks are too high and the water too deep, the wildebeest will not be able to climb out on the other side and become trapped. In most years, large numbers drown. Others are trampled to death or are snapped up by gigantic Nile crocodiles, and many are taken by lion prides that stake out the crossings. Elsewhere, they fall prey to cheetahs, African hunting dogs and hyenas, while others die of injury or exhaustion. In a typical year, over 250 000 wildebeest die along the journey from Tanzania to the Masai Mara.

BABY WILDEBEEST With its mother in attendance, a calf takes its first tentative steps. Every year, around 300 000 wildebeest are born in the southern Serengeti, just prior to the annual migration.

BLUE WILDEBEEST

ALL OF THE ONE MILLION OR MORE BLUE

WILDEBEEST IN THE SERENGETI MIGRATE EACH YEAR. So-called because of the conspicuous silvery blue sheen of its hide, the blue wildebeest is somewhat ungainly and can weigh up to 270 kg, but it nonetheless attains speeds of up to 65 km/h. Although it can tolerate arid regions, it requires a long drink every few days as well as access to short green grasses, to which its blunt muzzle is best adapted. It is because of these requirements that some wildebeest herds, such as those of the Serengeti, need to make extensive annual migrations.

One of the most striking features of the blue wildebeest is the territorial behaviour of the adult males, who mark the boundaries of their territories with scent and dung heaps. Neighbouring males compete at these boundaries through loud grunting, stamping, head-shaking and brief 'face-offs' in which they exchange horn thrusts. Once his territory is established, a male attempts to lure a female into his domain with displays that include rolling in the dust, bellowing and thrusting his horns into the ground or trees. The volume of noise in the Serengeti rutting season is extraordinary, both in amplitude and sheer variety of snorting, stamping and bellowing.

VITAL STATISTICS

CLASS: Mammalia
ORDER: Artiodactyla
SPECIES: *Connochaetes taurinus*
HABITAT: Grassland savannah
DISTRIBUTION: East and southern Africa
KEY FEATURES: High shoulders, cow-like horns, long black tail and mane, long-muzzled head

ZEBRA FIGHT Courtship and mating sometimes take place within herds during migrations. Here plains zebra stallions are fighting over access to a harem of females near Lake Nakuru in Kenya.

Caribou migration

In the far north of Canada and Alaska, migrations of caribou (reindeer) are thought to involve well over 2 million individual animals. Each spring they move from their wintering grounds in or around North America's boreal forests northwards towards their calving and feeding grounds in the Arctic tundra, where the spring vegetation appears earlier. The tundra is also relatively free of wolves and another nuisance that they wish to avoid: hordes of biting mosquitoes and midges.

The caribou's summer food includes sedges, grasses and willow leaves. In autumn, they flock south again towards the forests, where they forage under the snow for their winter food, which consists primarily of lichens, moss and a few small shrubs. The annual round trip is the longest migration of any land mammal in the world and in some cases totals more than 6000 km. Over the course of these journeys, the caribou will

not hesitate to swim across large lakes and broad rivers, and they occasionally perish in large numbers during these crossings.

Caribou travel in herds because they need to eat and watch for predators at the same time – to do so is much easier in a large group, where some individuals can stand sentry while the rest forage. In the Arctic calving grounds, the main predators are golden eagles, which can kill calves with their talons, and wolverines, which are capable of killing new-born calves or adult females giving birth. In winter, wolves are the most important predators. There is some evidence that male caribou avoid groups of females and their calves in winter because they know that wolves are drawn to the more vulnerable young.

About half of all reindeer in North America are of a type (subspecies) called barren-ground caribou. They are somewhat smaller and lighter coloured than the other main subspecies, the woodland caribou. Most barren-ground caribou live within one of seven or eight distinct herds, each of which migrate within fairly precisely defined regions that occupy parts of north-central Canada, the Northwest Territories, and the largest of the northern Canadian territories, Nunavut. The Beverly herd, for example – one of the largest – winters in northern Saskatchewan and Manitoba, and migrates in summer to west-central Nunavut. Each year, as it migrates south, this herd numbers over 400 000 individuals. Other barren-ground herds move around within overlapping ranges to the north, west and east. In addition, herds of other caribou subspecies migrate within other huge areas to the west and east – a subspecies called Grant's caribou forms what is known as the Porcupine caribou herd in Alaska and the northern Yukon, while migratory woodland caribou form two large herds in northern Quebec and Labrador.

Mongolian gazelles

The vast, unfenced steppes of eastern Mongolia are some of the last remaining and largest temperate grasslands in the world. They are home to the Mongolian gazelle, or zeren, a medium-sized golden-brown antelope that migrates annually between northern calving grounds and more southerly winter grounds spread throughout the region. The total population of the Mongolian gazelle is thought to be around 1.5 million, with herds ranging in size up to 8000 individuals.

Large herds containing both sexes begin to gather in spring to start their trek north, during which they may cover 200–300 km in a single day. These gazelles are both extremely fast runners, attaining speeds up to 65 km/h, and good swimmers, which boosts the speed of their migrations and helps them to avoid predators, such as wolves and lynx. In June and early July thousands of females find their way in small groups to a few traditional calving grounds, lush with green grass, to give birth. As winter approaches, the gazelles gather again in major herds to migrate south across the steppes.

Herds of Sudan

One of the world's largest migratory herds exists in a surprising place. In southern Sudan, despite several decades of civil war amongst the human population, some species of wildlife have not

KOB MOB This group of kob are on alert in long savannah grass in Virunga National Park in the Democratic Republic of the Congo.

FACTS
IN OCTOBER 2007, SOME 10 000 wildebeest drowned while attempting to cross Kenya's Mara River during an annual migration. Herd members had mistakenly picked a river crossing point with embankments that were too high for the animals to climb back out of the river onto dry land.

A HERD OF KOB and other ungulates spotted in southern Sudan in May 2007 formed a continuous mass of animals that was 80 km long and 30 km wide.

ONE CARIBOU HERD SPOTTED IN NORTHERN QUEBEC IN 2001 COMPRISED OVER 625 000 INDIVIDUALS.
FACTS

only survived but have thrived east of the River Nile in numbers that rival those of herds anywhere else in Africa.

In 2007, an aerial survey by the Wildlife Conservation Society (WCS) – the first survey in the area since 1982 – discovered a migratory herd of white-eared kob numbering some 800 000 animals. These medium-sized, chestnut-coloured antelopes seasonally travel hundreds of kilometres through grasslands and swamps while tracking the rainfall and seasonal inundation of the Nile Sudd. Accompanying the kob were other migratory species, including an estimated 250 000 Mongalla gazelle (a small tan-and-white antelope with a black stripe on its flank), 160 000 tiang and 13 000 reedbuck (both medium-sized, horned antelopes). The total number of animals was estimated at 1.3 million – quite remarkable for a region where wildlife was thought to have vanished.

Since it had been assumed that the civil war had led to environmental devastation, the discovery of this huge herd came as a happy surprise to conservationists. Unfortunately, some Sudanese species do appear to have suffered severe population declines – there were far fewer elephants, zebra and African buffalo than previously. The Wildlife Conservation Society now wants to build on the survey findings to preserve the extraordinary wildlife that they found.

SERVICE STATIONS

EVERY NOVEMBER, TENS OF THOUSANDS OF AVIAN VISITORS descend on the DeSoto National Wildlife Refuge near Missouri Valley in the American prairie state of Iowa. They are snow geese en route from their breeding areas in the Arctic tundra of northern Canada. In some years, more than 500 000 geese, together with other migratory waterfowl, congregate in the Refuge. There they form a great white blanket over part of DeSoto Lake and create an amazing spectacle each morning as they erupt in their tens of thousands into the crimson-coloured dawn sky.

The geese are only temporary visitors to the DeSoto Refuge, using it as a refuelling stop or 'service station' during a 3000 km migration that will eventually take them to wintering grounds along the Gulf Coast of Texas and Louisiana. During the stopover, the birds rest and replenish their energy reserves, foraging for waste grain in nearby fields. At dusk they return to DeSoto Lake, where they spend the night safe from predators. But once it starts snowing, or temperatures drop below freezing, they resume their voyage south.

For many of the geese DeSoto is just one of several pitstops that they make during the long migration – lakes in North Dakota and Missouri are other resting places. Throughout the migration, they stay together in flocks of 100 to 1000 birds, made up of many family groups. Typically the whole flock flies in an imperfect V-formation. Travelling en masse in this way has advantages for the group, as their overall energy expenditure is less than would be the case if each goose flew on its own (see page 126). Effectively, this means that they can make longer flights between stopovers.

Delaware Bay

Each spring, an estimated 300 000 to 600 000 waders descend on the beaches of Delaware Bay on the east coast of North America to refresh and refuel. In some years, for a peak period around the end of May, as many as 220 000 birds converge at the same time. They include migrants from the south-eastern USA and Gulf of Mexico, including least sandpipers, dunlin and ruddy turnstones, and others that have

SNOW GEESE A huge flock of migratory snow geese has gathered on a lake in New Mexico.

AT THE WATER'S EDGE In a corner of Delaware Bay, a group of laughing gulls waits for some horseshoe crabs to start spawning.

flown all the way from Central or South America, including red knots (from southern Argentina and Tierra del Fuego), and sanderlings (from Brazil, Peru and Chile). Also present are large numbers of laughing gulls and least terns.

Another important stopover site on the east coast of North America is the upper Bay of Fundy, in Nova Scotia, Canada, where hundreds of thousands of semipalmated sandpipers and other shorebirds break their journey each year to feed on a tiny crustacean that lives in the tidal mudflats.

Stopovers such as these are especially important for the migratory waders, which travel as much as 30 000 km per year and must take advantage of seasonally abundant food reserves where they can. Many of the waders synchronise their visits to Delaware Bay, for example, with the emergence of tens of thousands of horseshoe crabs from the sea. The crabs deposit their eggs on the beach, and the birds eat them. Without this refuelling stop, the birds would not make it to their breeding grounds further north – some need to double their body weight in a matter of about three weeks before they can resume their journeys. Unfortunately, in recent years there has been a marked decline in the number of horseshoe crabs coming ashore in Delaware Bay, since many are now caught and killed by humans for use as bait in the conch and eel-fishing industries. This has led to a serious decline in the numbers of some of the waders,

especially red knots, to such an extent that the American subspecies of this bird is now considered in danger of extinction.

Eurasian stopovers

On the vast Kola Peninsula in north-western Russia, willow grouse migrate in 300-strong flocks along valleys where the scrub provides relatively safe stopovers to feed and rest. The flocks may pass for several days, but they do not go unnoticed. Gyrfalcons and snowy owls stake out the resting sites.

Eastern Mongolia and north-eastern China contain a number of important stopover points for Siberian cranes as they migrate along a 5000 km route from north-eastern Siberia to central China. These resting areas are wetlands, where the cranes can refuel on a variety of plants and fish. Although some of the wetlands are now protected by nature reserves, such as those at Zhalong and Xianghai, others remain unprotected.

In Europe, 30 000 common cranes descend annually on the Hortobágy wetlands in Hungary as a stopover on their autumn migration from northern Europe. Hortobágy is an area of lakes, streams and fish ponds, caused by regular flooding of the River Tisza in what is otherwise an area of dry grassland. The cranes arrive in October and, depending on the weather, typically stay for a month. During the day they feed on the nearby cultivated lands, picking up corn seeds, but also catching and eating insects, frogs and even small rodents. In the first week of November, groups of them start departing for the southern part of the Hungarian Plain, from where they continue on towards their wintering sites in Tunisia and Sudan.

SANDHILL CRANES

EACH SPRING, ONE OF THE GREATEST

AVIAN SPECTACLES ON EARTH TAKES PLACE ON THE PLATTE RIVER IN NEBRASKA, USA. Upwards of 450 000 sandhill cranes – almost 90 per cent of the world's population – fly in for a stopover on their way from wintering sites in Mexico, Texas and New Mexico. They do so partly just to rest and partly to fatten up before resuming their 10 000 km long migration to marshy breeding areas in Canada, Alaska and Siberia. Lean on arrival, each crane acquires about 500 grams of fat during its spring sojourn in Nebraska.

The cranes, which have a grey body that may be stained reddish, start to arrive in early March and continue doing so for two to three weeks. Every evening, flight after flight appears out of the southern skies, then circles in to land and roost on one of the many sandbars on the broad, shallow reaches of the Platte River. There they roost for the night, typically standing in water about 10 cm deep. At the crack of dawn, the sandhill cranes depart from these roosts in their tens of thousands to visit nearby fields, where they feed on a mixture of corn and small invertebrate animals, such as snails and worms. On their return later in the day, the cacophony of squawking and bugling calls, both from on high and from the sandbars, can be deafening. Roosting densities can be as high as 12 000 cranes per kilometre of river.

Fossil evidence indicates that sandhill cranes have been making stopovers in Nebraska for several million years.

VITAL STATISTICS

CLASS: Aves
ORDER: Gruiformes
SPECIES: *Grus canadensis*
HABITAT: Open grasslands, meadows and wetlands
DISTRIBUTION: North America, north-eastern Siberia
KEY FEATURE: Up to 1.3 m tall, with a wingspan of around 1.7 m

SAFETY
NUMBERS

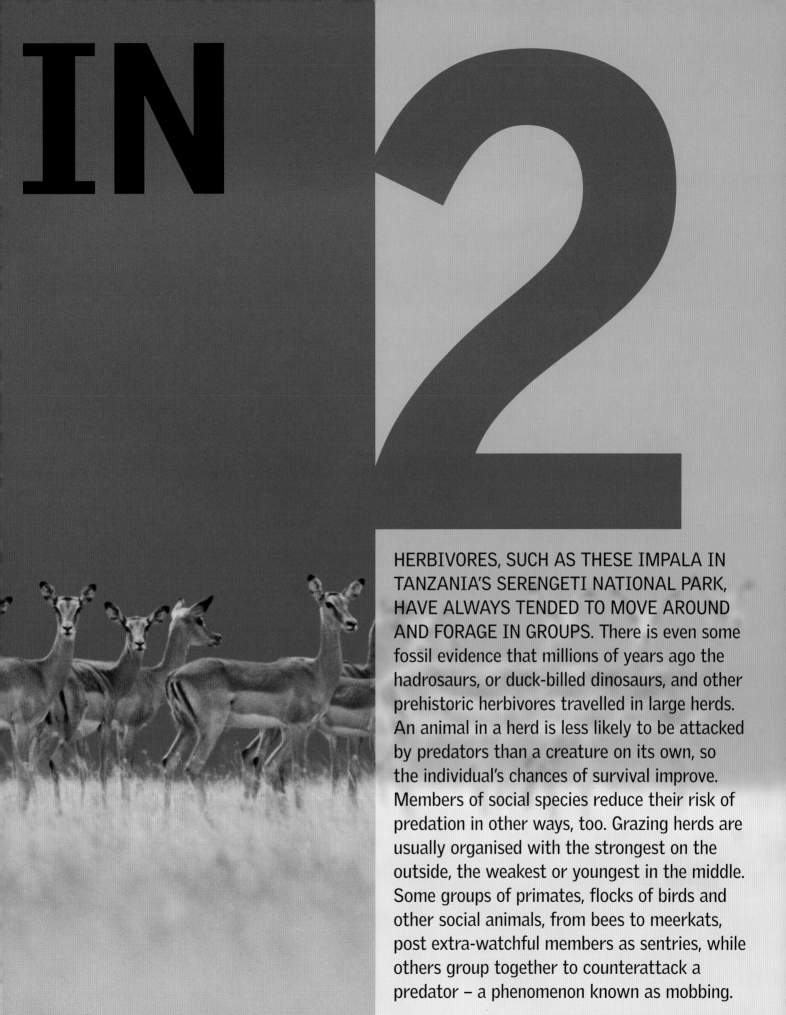

IN 2

HERBIVORES, SUCH AS THESE IMPALA IN TANZANIA'S SERENGETI NATIONAL PARK, HAVE ALWAYS TENDED TO MOVE AROUND AND FORAGE IN GROUPS. There is even some fossil evidence that millions of years ago the hadrosaurs, or duck-billed dinosaurs, and other prehistoric herbivores travelled in large herds. An animal in a herd is less likely to be attacked by predators than a creature on its own, so the individual's chances of survival improve. Members of social species reduce their risk of predation in other ways, too. Grazing herds are usually organised with the strongest on the outside, the weakest or youngest in the middle. Some groups of primates, flocks of birds and other social animals, from bees to meerkats, post extra-watchful members as sentries, while others group together to counterattack a predator – a phenomenon known as mobbing.

DEFENSIVE FORMATION

DEFENSIVE WALLS AND CIRCLES, MASS CHARGES AND SYNCHRONISED MOVEMENT ARE AMONG THE MANY DEFENCES DEPLOYED BY GROUP-LIVING ANIMALS. A classic example is the musk ox – a large, thick-coated, bovine animal that lives in groups of 10–20 in the frozen Arctic tundra. When a herd is threatened by wolves or a grizzly bear, the adults stand shoulder-to-shoulder in a line (against a lone predator) or in a compact circle (against a group of predators), facing outwards, with the youngsters in the centre. With their heads lowered and horns pointing towards their attackers, they create an impenetrable wall. On occasions, one or more oxen charge an attacker. Although these tactics are effective against animal predators, they make the musk oxen an easy target for human hunters.

Counterattack!

African, or Cape, buffalo – considered by some people to be the most dangerous animals in Africa – go further. When a group of buffalo is harassed by a pride of lions, the adults form a line with the larger individuals at the front and youngsters behind. But instead of waiting for an attack, the buffalo advance en masse, attempting to scare off the predators or even to injure and incapacitate them. Lions confronted by these

Instead of waiting for an attack, African buffalo advance en masse, attempting to scare off predators or even to injure and incapacitate them. Lions confronted by these counterattacks are sometimes severely trampled or gored.

LINE OF DEFENCE With their huge bulk, large horns and threatening posture, musk oxen produce a formidable barrier around their young.

FISHBALLING Striped catfish off the east coast of Australia form a compact school. It is tempting to speculate that they are trying to resemble a single, larger fish.

counterattacks are sometimes severely trampled or gored. In one incident witnessed in South Africa, a group of five lionesses who had ambushed a juvenile buffalo were chased off by a rampaging herd of 30 adults, one of the lionesses being flung some 4 m into the air on a brandished buffalo horn.

Wall of walrus

Walrus gather on peninsulas and islands in the Arctic. Like the musk oxen, they protect their young from attack by placing their great bulk in the way, forming a barrier. Polar bears are shrugged off with a shake of the body. Some bears employ a counter-strategy of rushing crowded walrus beaches in the hope that some individuals will panic and start a stampede, inevitably leading to a few walrus – the infirm or young – being crushed or wounded in the commotion. Bears then take full advantage, although even an injured walrus is a formidable opponent for a polar bear owing to its great weight and massive tusks.

Insect posturing

Some insects also employ defensive postures. There are types of sawfly larvae that stay together and, if they are threatened by a larger insect, raise their heads in unison to scare off the attacker. Some types of beetle larvae, when resting between bouts of feeding, may arrange themselves in rosette-shaped (cycloalexic) formations. The formations maximise body contact between the larvae, allowing signals to radiate rapidly through the group and alert members to danger. If enough larva join these formations, they are protected from attacks on all sides.

Fish formations

In the subaquatic world, well over 80 per cent of fish school, or form a compact group or ball, when predators are about. One possible explanation for this tactic is that potential predators may be given the impression they are facing one vast, frightening fish. In some species the fish face outwards, baring their teeth, an example being the various South American river species known as piranhas. Often thought of as aggressive carnivores that launch into a feeding frenzy at the first taste of blood, the piranhas' behaviour is more often a defence mechanism against larger predators such as river dolphins and crocodiles.

In a mob of meerkats, one or more adults stand guard, looking out for predators while others forage or play. Sentry duty lasts approximately one hour.

ANIMALS THAT LIVE IN LARGE COMMUNITIES BENEFIT FROM THE MANY PAIRS OF EYES CONSTANTLY SCANNING FOR DANGER. In some species, roles are differentiated, with one or two individuals acting as lookouts while the majority forage or rest. This type of behaviour is commonly seen in meerkats or suricates – small, mongoose-like mammals that inhabit the Kalahari Desert in southern Africa.

In a mob of meerkats, one or more adults stand guard, looking out for predators while others forage or play. Sentry duty lasts approximately one hour.

SENTRY DUTY

The meerkat guards make shrill chirping sounds when all is well, but if they spot danger, such as an approaching eagle or jackal, they bark loudly or whistle. The rest of the mob, which usually numbers around 20, retreat into one of their many burrows. When the threat has passed, the sentries reappear and check that the predator really has gone, constantly barking to keep the others underground. When the sentries are satisfied that all is safe they stop barking, and the others emerge.

Sentry benefits

Biologists once thought that sentry behaviour in meerkats was purely altruistic. A sentry seems to put itself at greater risk of being snapped up by a predator while missing out on the opportunity to feed. But although a sentry might appear to have a reduced chance of survival compared to the foraging group, in terms of ensuring the survival of its genes into the next generation, this behaviour considerably enhances the survival of others in the sentry's mob – its brothers, sisters and offspring – with which it shares many genes.

More recently, scientists have concluded that the benefits of sentry behaviour may be more complex. Observations of meerkat mobs have shown that the sentries are hardly ever taken by predators, whereas their foraging companions occasionally are, so being a sentry may actually be one of the safest things a meerkat can do to improve its chances of survival. There even appears to be some competition for sentry duty among adult meerkats, and many sentries have recently enjoyed hearty meals. Animal behaviourists have speculated that being a sentry may be a type of prestige indicator in meerkats – a mark that an individual is an efficient forager and so able to perform other activities. This may help sentry meerkats to attract more mates.

Other sentinels

Sentry, or sentinel, behaviour is a feature of the social life of many animals. Bee colonies often have sentries posted outside the entrance, while any attempt to sneak up on a troop of baboons is invariably thwarted by a vigilant sentinel. Dwarf mongoose males that are low in the hierarchy make up a rearguard, keeping watch from behind as the group hunts for food. If a predator appears, these rear sentinels are often killed as they run to catch up with their escaping companions.

Cotton-top tamarins – small monkeys that live in the tropical forests of northern Colombia – take turns as sentries. These animals live in small groups of about three to nine individuals in defended territories. When the group is foraging or resting, one adult acts as a lookout, constantly scanning for potential predators above and around the group. On spotting danger, it deploys some of its repertory of 38 distinct sounds to warn the others.

ALERT TO DANGER In the Kalahari Desert of Botswana, a small mob of meerkats scan the horizon for predators. By taking its turn as lookout, a meerkat can help to lengthen its own lifespan as well as that of fellow mob members.

BIRD SENTRIES

Several bird species exhibit sentinel behaviour. Groups of scrub jays in Florida invariably post a lookout on a telephone wire or up a tall tree while they forage on the ground. Myna birds (such as the Asian pied myna, below) are known to stand sentry and squawk a warning to their mates and even to other birds when a predator is nearby. The Arabian babbler, a songbird that inhabits the Middle East, has taken sentry duty to new heights. In this species, great prestige appears to be attached to being a lookout. It is a duty that tends to be monopolised by the dominant male in the group, and he may even buy off a rival for the post by offering it food to displace it from the sentry post.

ALARM!

MOST ANIMALS THAT LIVE TOGETHER USE A RANGE OF ALARM CALLS TO COMMUNICATE DANGER TO OTHER MEMBERS OF THE SAME SPECIES. The gelada, a species of monkey found in the highlands of Ethiopia, issues a particular alarm call to indicate the presence of a predator, which may be a leopard, hyena or human. An adult male gelada makes a deep, two-phased bark that sounds like a 'wahoo', which it then repeats at two to five-second intervals. Female and juvenile geladas make sharper, shriller, more explosive calls. Either call usually causes all members of the troop to flee to the cliff-face caves and ledges where they habitually sleep at night.

Alarm calls are issued by all sorts of animals, but they are most common among birds, primates, rodents and deer that live or forage in groups or pairs and have specific predators. Most birds' alarm calls are high frequency and difficult for a predator to pinpoint. For example, the blackbird's characteristic alarm call (a 'pook pook pook' chirp) and the robin's (a sharp 'tick tick' call) are familiar sounds in gardens, and often indicate the presence of a prowling cat.

Specific calls

Some animals produce warning signals that are specific to the type of predator. The vervet monkeys of East Africa use different, distinctive calls to indicate the presence of leopards, snakes and eagles. As soon as the call is given, each member of the troop knows where to look for danger and what type

WATCHFUL DAD
A male gelada bares his teeth as he stands guard over his family. His alarm call is a deep, loud bark.

of evasive action to take. In response to a leopard alarm call, the monkeys climb to the smallest branches in their trees, where they are safely out of reach of the relatively heavy predator. If they hear the snake alarm they scan the ground, while the eagle alarm sends them scrambling deep within their trees or diving into dense bushes.

Some monkey species are more alert than others, so unrelated species tend to travel and forage with the watchful ones. Diana monkeys of West Africa are especially vigilant, so olive colobus and red colobus monkeys join them. Yellow-casqued hornbills may also attach themselves to the group. All the monkey species and the hornbills share a common foe – the crowned hawk eagle – and the Diana monkeys have a specific alarm call should one appear. But if the Diana monkeys emit their leopard alarm call the hornbills ignore it, as leopards are only interested in the monkeys.

Similarly, chital deer, which inhabit woodlands and forest on the Indian subcontinent, benefit from the alarm calls of the common langur monkey should a tiger approach. The monkeys, in turn, benefit from the chital's keen sense of smell and respond to the deer's alarm calls.

Benefits of alarms

Alarm signals obviously help to prolong the lives of listeners, but alarm-calling might seem to come at a cost to the caller. When an animal signals alarm, it draws attention to itself, so it may be more easily spotted by the predator than its companions. Why so many animals should engage in alarm-calling when the behaviour seems to be self-sacrificing has sparked fierce debate among evolutionary biologists. One widely held explanation, based on the premise that natural selection takes place at the level of genes, is that although sounding the alarm may be disadvantageous to the individual, the behaviour is likely to persist if it helps to save the alarm-caller's relatives, which share its genes.

VOCAL VERVET The specific alarm calls issued by vervet monkeys for different predators are a mixture of barking, chattering, chirping and screaming sounds.

Other researchers have found that some species stay silent in situations where alarm-calling will put the caller or the colony at increased risk from a predator. Pikas (also called coneys, or 'whistling hares' due to their high-pitched alarm calls) immediately dive into their burrows on hearing an alarm call, but they only make these calls when they spot predators such as hawks and pine martens, which cannot follow them into their burrows. When pikas spot weasels, they stay silent, unwilling to attract the attention of this voracious small predator that can enter their burrows. Another theory suggests that alarm signals function as a deterrent, communicating alertness and so putting off the predator.

Chemical alarms

Not all alarm signals are transmitted by sound. Many animals, particularly fish and insects, use chemical alarm signals communicated by the release of substances known as pheromones. When alarmed, smelt (a kind of fish) secrete a pheromone into the water that warns other members of the school. Injured minnows and catfish release alarm pheromones that cause others nearby to hide in dense schools near the bottom. When a

honeybee stings an intruder in the hive, it releases isoamyl acetate, a fruity-smelling substance that excites other bees to join the attack. If a predator attacks an aphid on a leaf, the aphid releases an alarm pheromone that causes other aphids to drop off the plant to the ground.

Some plants release alarm chemicals of their own. When infested with spider mites, lima bean plants release a messenger chemical that can be detected by nearby plants of the same species. The chemical causes the recipient plants to prepare themselves by activating genes that control the release of substances distasteful to mites, making themselves less vulnerable to mite attack. The same messenger chemical also attracts another mite species that is a predator of spider mites.

False alarms

Some bird species have been observed making false alarm calls in circumstances where they can gain an advantage. Thrushes have been known to make counterfeit alarm calls to frighten other birds away from an area where they want to feed. Male swallows have been observed making false alarm calls during the mating season to discourage their female partners from leaving the nesting area. The presumed purpose of the deception is to prevent the female from mating with other males in the area.

PIKA LOOKOUT These small animals rely on their sharp eyesight and sensitive hearing to spot potential predators and give an alarm call to the colony.

MOBBING

COOPERATIVE COUNTERATTACK AND HARASSMENT ARE TWO OF THE MOST EFFECTIVE METHODS that a group of animals can use to drive away a predator or competitor. The behaviour, called mobbing, is widespread throughout the animal kingdom. The greater the number of participants, the more successful the tactic is likely to be, and mobbing calls may be used to summon individuals nearby to cooperate in the attack.

A mob of birds

Mobbing behaviour was first recognised and studied in birds. When birds see an interloper, they emit alarm calls and then fly at the intruder, squawking loudly, dive-bombing and harassing it. Sometimes they make physical contact. Usually, just one or two mobbers are involved at first, but others may join in, including members of other species. Mobbing tends to occur most intensely on breeding grounds and in the breeding season, so its main function is probably to distract predators and prevent them locating nests containing eggs or young birds.

Mobbing has been recorded in a wide range of species, but it is particularly well developed in birds that breed in colonies, such as gulls and terns. These and a few other

When birds see an interloper, they emit alarm calls and then fly at the intruder, squawking loudly, dive-bombing and harassing it. Sometimes they make physical contact.

HERON HARASSMENT Avocets chase away a grey heron in Norfolk. Avocet mobbing often culminates in dive-bombing the intruder.

species, such as blackbirds and swallows, typically mob eagles and buzzards. Songbirds mob owls, while avocets chase off any other birds that try to nest near them. Many birds mob cuckoos because of the special threat they pose. Herons are frequently mobbed, possibly because their large silhouettes in flight cause them to be mistaken for birds of prey. Terns and skuas mob terrestrial predators such as mink, foxes, snakes and even humans. As well as flying at a predator and making alarm calls, some birds also defecate or vomit on the predator with astonishing accuracy. There are reports of predators being grounded by the weight of droppings deposited on them after intensive mobbing by fieldfares.

There are some risks for birds, or other animals, engaging in mobbing: they expend a lot of energy, and there is a danger that the intruder will turn on one of them. But as well as protecting offspring and eggs, mobbing behaviour may teach young how to recognise predator or competitor species, it may injure the intruder, and it may advertise a mobbing bird's physical fitness both to the intruder and to prospective mates.

Dicing with death

Many mammal species also engage in mobbing. Meerkats mob snakes and hawks, while banded mongoose gang up to mob jackals. Cape fur seals and Australian fur seals mob great white sharks. California ground squirrels follow a highly idiosyncratic routine when mobbing rattlesnakes: they distract the snake from locating their burrows by kicking sand in its eyes.

Various species of baboons group together to mob their main predators, which include lions, leopards and pythons. Large male baboons threaten lions by shaking branches and giving alarm barks; they confront leopards by flashing their eyelids, yawning to show their teeth and gesturing. If a leopard has attacked a baboon, other members of the victim's troop may become considerably more aggressive, running up and scuffing the leopard and chasing it away. A leopard has been observed feigning death after a severe mobbing by a troop of 30 baboons. Experimental evidence suggests that chimpanzees also mob leopards: when faced with a mechanical leopard installed in a forest clearing, a group of chimpanzees screamed, stamped their feet and threw objects at the 'predator'.

Shoal power

Fish occasionally harass intruders in their territory in ways that are reminiscent of mobbing by birds or mammals, especially in the way the fish act as a coordinated group. Groups of bluegill sunfish (a North American freshwater species) have been seen mobbing snapping turtles, swimming rapidly up to the turtles and following them across their breeding territories while staying out of snapping range. French grunts have been observed harassing a barracuda by swimming behind it and nipping at its tail. Damselfish are extremely aggressive and intolerant of any other marine life straying into their territories, and attack all but the biggest predators. Damselfish occupying neighbouring territories on a coral reef will often gang up to repel an intruder.

TURNING TAIL A leopard being driven off by a group of olive baboons in the Masai Mara Game Reserve in Kenya.

SHARK SCHOOLS

YOUNG SHARKS ARE VULNERABLE TO PREDATION – USUALLY FROM BIGGER SHARKS AND ORCAS (KILLER WHALES) – and so take refuge in groups or schools. But scalloped hammerheads continue to form schools as adults, even though they are too large to have many predators.

Scalloped hammerheads are found in tropical and warm temperate waters around the world. They have been seen schooling in the Sea of Cortez (Gulf of California), off the Galápagos Islands and Cocos Island in the Pacific, in the Red Sea and around Hawaii. The structure and purpose of the schools appear to vary between locations.

Schooltime

In the Sea of Cortez, scalloped hammerheads form immense schools of up to several hundred individuals, usually at depths of 10–50 m, and most often over seamounts. The gatherings take place during daylight, and the sharks swim together, evenly spaced a few metres apart. At night they hunt alone.

Researchers have offered several explanations why hammerheads collect in these massive groups. The seamounts are conveniently close to rich food supplies, so the sharks may simply be congregating in relatively safe places between hunting forays – a behaviour known as refuging. But the schools also seem to have a social function. They consist mainly of young females, who use a complex body language to jostle for the most prominent positions at the centre of the group.

A different structure has been observed in scalloped hammerhead schools in the Red Sea. Here, juveniles and adults school together, with the smallest and

SHARK SCHOOL Silhouetted against the electric blue of the ocean surface, a school of scalloped hammerheads soar in a stately parade.

In the Sea of Cortez, scalloped hammerhead sharks form immense schools of up to several hundred individuals, usually at depths of 10–50 m, and most often over seamounts.

youngest near the centre and the adults around the outside; the very largest females cruise the periphery. It seems that the main purpose of this schooling behaviour is to protect the young from predation. Some researchers have suggested that the high density of predators in the Red Sea might be responsible for the defensive formation.

Schooling behaviour may have additional functions in some cases, such as providing a prelude to mating. Female hammerheads can display their relative size to male suitors, while shaking their heads to drive younger females away.

Sociable sharks

Although scalloped hammerheads are the only large sharks known to form big schools, other species refuge between foraging trips. Nursehounds (greater spotted dogfish) gather beneath rocky overhangs, as do whitetip reef sharks. At Bikini Atoll in the south-west Pacific, grey reef sharks congregate in a channel known locally as 'Shark Alley'. The current here during the outgoing and incoming tides keeps oxygenated water flowing through their gills, so they use less energy while resting.

SCALLOPED HAMMERHEADS FOLLOW TINY MAGNETIC variations in the surface of the sea floor to navigate between their refuging grounds around seamounts and their feeding grounds.

9 DIFFERENT types of display behaviour have been observed in the Sea of Cortez hammerheads.

THE LARGEST REFUGING SCHOOL OF HAMMERHEADS ever observed – in the Sea of Cortez – contained more than 500 individuals.

FACTS

CLUSTERS FOR WINTER

FACED WITH STRONG WINDS AND FREEZING TEMPERATURES DURING WINTER, many animals cluster together to keep warm. Some form huddles to cut down on heat loss, and thus on the rate at which they deplete their internal energy stores, through close body contact – a tactic known as social thermoregulation. Others seek out specific microclimates that will help them to survive the winter. If this microclimate is limited to a small area, the animals naturally crowd together.

Huddling penguins

In Antarctica, female emperor penguins lay their eggs in mid-May, about five weeks before the darkest, coldest days of winter. They then leave the eggs in the care of the males and depart to spend the next two months feeding at sea. For about 65 days each

CLOSE COMPANIONS A huge group of male emperor penguins crowd together for warmth while incubating their eggs. All the males take turns to stand on the outside of the group.

MACAQUE TRIO In northern Japan, where winter temperatures can reach –15°C, macaques snuggle together in sleeping groups that grow larger as the temperature drops.

male penguin incubates an egg, which rests on its feet enveloped in an insulating fold of skin and fat that hangs from the abdomen. Throughout this task the males have no choice but to fast, while coping with winds of up to 200 km/h and wind-chill temperatures that drop to -60°C. To reduce the rate at which they lose heat and deplete their energy stores, they huddle together.

Huddles of emperor penguins typically consist of several hundred birds packed together in densities as high as 10 penguins per square metre of ground. Within the huddle, individual penguins seem temporarily to lose their identity, and the whole mass takes on the behaviour and appearance of a single living entity. Huddling cuts the rate at which individuals lose heat by as much as 50 per cent, and is thus vital in helping them to survive the long winter. About two-thirds of the slowdown in heat loss is due to the reduction in the area of body surface exposed to the cold, and one-third is due to the mild microclimate created within the huddling groups. The temperature inside an emperor penguin huddle can reach an astonishing 24°C.

For the individual, huddling is not just a matter of selfishly trying to stay in the warmest position. The penguins take turns in occupying the warmest and coldest positions, behaviour that requires a degree of cooperation. During a blizzard, those on the windward edge of the huddle feel the cold most keenly. One by one they peel off and shuffle, eggs on feet, down the sides of the huddle to rejoin on the downwind side. Then they follow one another in a continuous procession through the warm centre of the huddle, eventually returning back to the windward edge. As a result of this constant circulation, the whole huddle gradually moves downwind. During a 48-hour blizzard, a huddle can shift as much as 200 m.

Snuggling skunks

Some striped skunks huddle together for warmth during winter – and it seems that they emerge stronger than loners. While most male skunks hibernate alone, groups of female skunks often snuggle together with one male in a communal den. Comparative studies have shown that the huddling skunks emerge in spring with higher fat stores as a percentage of body-weight – about 25 per cent – compared with only about 10 per cent for solitary skunks. This is because snuggling helps to insulate the skunks against heat loss and so reduces the rate at which they burn up their fat reserves. It also reduces water loss. In early spring, relatively high levels of body fat help to sustain these skunks until the plants they eat begin to flourish. For female skunks, improved body condition is also important for the spring gestation and lactation periods.

Two other North American mammals that, like striped skunks, often use social thermoregulation to keep warm in winter

LADYBIRD BALL A group of a hundred or so 12-spotted ladybirds hibernating on a pine-needle cluster in a Californian forest.

are raccoons and southern flying squirrels. The record number of raccoons found in a single underground winter den is 23 (of which only one was a male), while a tree cavity in Illinois was once found to contain 50 flying squirrels.

Basking butterflies

Every winter, a remarkable spectacle takes place high in the mountains of central Mexico and the central coastal region of California. Up to 100 million colourful monarch butterflies gather to spend the winter in a few selected pockets of forest. These butterflies have migrated for up to 2500 km from more northerly latitudes to escape the winter cold, flying at altitudes as high as 3000 m. To survive, they require overwintering sites with

BUTTERFLY TREES The trunks of these oyamel firs in the Mexican highlands are completely covered in hibernating monarch butterflies.

specific microclimatic attributes: a winter temperature range of 0–15°C – cold enough to encourage hibernation but not so cold that the butterflies use up their fat reserves – and a humidity range that ensures they do not dry out. They also require trees to supply the substrate for winter roosting and a forest canopy for protection during winter storms.

Sites fulfilling these requirements are restricted to forests of oyamel fir at an elevation of 2400–3600 m. Monarchs that breed east of the Rocky Mountains overwinter in the high mountains of central Mexico, while those from west of the Rockies migrate to the California coast. On arrival, they crowd onto every available tree surface – some trees become so laden that branches bend, and occasionally break, under the weight. The butterfly clusters look like massive clumps of feathery, orange-and-black grapes. Each butterfly hangs with its wings over the butterfly beneath it, creating a shingle effect that buffers them from rain and creates warmth. The weight of the clusters prevents the butterflies being blown away.

Some ladybirds become gregarious as winter approaches and huddle in large clusters that may consist of several hundred individuals. The reason for this behaviour is not known, but heat conservation is the most likely explanation.

Resting reptiles

Group hibernation is common among reptiles, especially snakes and some tortoises and turtles. In North America, racer snakes are one of the commonest species to gather together in winter, returning to the same den year after year. Timber rattlesnakes hibernate in dens containing up to 200 individuals, sometimes for up to seven months a year depending on latitude (the further north they live, the longer they hibernate). Sometimes they share dens with other snakes, such as northern copperheads and black rat snakes. Red-sided garter snakes form the largest hibernating snake communities in the world.

Wood turtles hibernate together underwater in streams and beaver ponds, even though they spend much of their waking life on land. Desert tortoises hibernate together in enlarged ground-squirrel burrows.

RED-SIDED GARTER SNAKE

THE LARGEST CONCENTRATION OF SNAKES

IN THE WORLD OCCURS EACH WINTER IN THE PROVINCE OF MANITOBA in Canada when red-sided garter snakes assemble to hibernate. Altogether, some 50 000 snakes gather for warmth in communal dens in a variety of environments, including caves, rock piles, sinkholes, sewers and the burrow systems of other animals. It is only by amassing below the frost line that these snakes can survive the harsh Manitoba winter.

Some of the wintering dens are quite small, containing no more than a few hundred snakes; others are vast. Four major dens have been identified in Manitoba's Narcisse Wildlife Management Area, each providing a temporary home for more than 5000 snakes. The dens consist of a network of crevasses and caverns formed by underground water that eroded the local limestone.

In spring, waves of snakes emerge. As each female appears, she is pursued by a number of males that entwine themselves around her, forming a mating ball. The young are born in late summer and spend their first winter in burrows and crevasses below the frost line. In their second year they migrate to one of the established communal dens.

VITAL STATISTICS

CLASS: Reptilia
ORDER: Squamata
SPECIES: *Thamnophis sirtalis parietalis*
HABITAT: Woodland, grassland, urban areas, usually near water
DISTRIBUTION: Central and western Canada to midwestern USA
KEY FEATURE: Dark body with red marks down sides, non-venomous

DUSK TO DAWN EMERGENCE

EVERY SUMMER EVENING, HUNDREDS OF PEOPLE GATHER IN AUSTIN, TEXAS, TO SEE THE WORLD'S LARGEST COLONY OF URBAN BATS. These metropolitan flyers – belonging to a species called the Mexican free-tailed bat – live in crevices beneath the Congress Avenue Bridge in downtown Austin.

Shortly before sunset they create an amazing show as up to 1.5 million bats come streaming out from their daytime roosts, reaching speeds of up to 100 km/h. The most spectacular flights occur during hot, dry August nights, when multiple columns of bats emerge. Blanketing the sky, they venture out to forage for insects, sometimes climbing to heights of 3300 m and travelling for hundreds of kilometres into the surrounding countryside. By the time the bats return at dawn, each one has typically eaten 3–8 g of flying insects. For the entire bat community, this amounts to between 4.5 and 12 tonnes of insects consumed in a single night.

BRIDGE OF BATS Watched by a throng of spectators, huge columns of Mexican free-tailed bats fly out from their roosts beneath Congress Avenue Bridge in Austin, Texas.

A species common to Mexico and the south-western United States, Mexican free-tailed bats belong to the group called microbats, which includes all bat species other than fruit bats. The adult bats are about 9 cm long and weigh just 15 g. Each spring, they migrate from central Mexico to various roosting sites throughout the south-western USA to give birth and take advantage of the thriving insect population.

Their sensational dusk emergences in Austin began in 1980, when the Congress Avenue Bridge was refurbished – the new design created narrow but deep openings underneath the structure that were ideal for the bats to roost in. At first, local residents were terrified by the vast clouds of bats that invaded the skies above the town every night – and dismayed by the large amounts of bat guano (droppings) deposited in and around the bridge, together with the accompanying smell. But people have since come to appreciate these flying mammals: by keeping the local mosquito population down to reasonable proportions, the throng of bats provides a valuable service to the Austin community. While in flight, each Mexican free-tailed bat can catch about 1200 mosquito-sized insects every hour.

The preference of microbats such as Mexican free-taileds for foraging at night is due to a combination of factors. Bat wings are so thin that they would dry out in strong sunlight, but more importantly, at night bats can avoid predators, particularly birds of prey, that lurk around their roosting sites. Avian predators, even owls, have great difficulty catching bats at night, except when the moon is bright. Over millions of years, microbats have exploited this, evolving a method of locating their own prey by echolocation, which works just as well at night as during the day, and also helps them to avoid colliding with other objects in the dark, moving or stationary. And by leaving and entering their roosts in mass formation, individual bats improve their chances of avoiding predation.

Bracken Cave bats

Although huge, the Austin bat colony is easily eclipsed by an even larger colony of Mexican free-taileds situated some 100 km to the south-west, at Bracken Cave near San Antonio. Bracken Cave hosts not just the world's biggest bat colony, but also the largest congregation of mammals anywhere in the world, consisting of between 20 and 40 million individual bats. Like their cousins in Austin, the Bracken Cave bats roost during the day and emerge at dusk. The colony can take several hours to make an orderly exit from the cave, creating what looks like a massive dark vortex rising into the air that is sometimes visible on air-traffic radar. Thick ribbons of hungry bats snake across the darkening skies while owls and red-tailed hawks occasionally dive into the columns in the twilight, snatching the unwary or unlucky. Every night the Bracken Cave bats devour some 200 tonnes of flying insects, many of them pests such as bollworm moths that otherwise would wreak millions of dollars of damage on the region's crops. On their return, the bats pack the roof and walls of Bracken Cave at a density of up to 2000 animals per square metre, raising the temperature inside the cave from 18 to 42°C.

Bats have been occupying Bracken Cave every summer for over 10 000 years. Most of the colony are females: the males live in separate caves nearby. In late June, a single pup is born to each female, nearly doubling the bat population of Bracken Cave over a period of a few weeks. Before leaving her infant, each mother spends up to an hour getting acquainted with its cry and scent. When she returns, by a remarkable feat she invariably manages to find her own offspring among the millions of others. For the baby bats, learning to fly at the age of a few weeks is precarious, since collisions with other bats or cave walls can be lethal. A crash landing on the cave floor means certain death because the floor is infested with millions of carnivorous beetles and other insects that can reduce an injured young bat to a skeleton within minutes. By mid-summer, the number of organisms living on the cave floor can reach astronomical proportions, and as they scurry about looking for food the floor is in a state of constant, seething motion.

The floor of Bracken Cave is also covered in large quantities of bat guano, which accumulates at the rate of 80 to 85 tonnes per year. The guano and the waste products of the beetles and other cave-floor dwellers together produce

CAVE COMMUNITY The floors of bat-inhabited caves are populated with a mass of invertebrates, such as this albino isopod (a small crustacean).

BAT SPECIALIST A bat hawk pounces on a flock of bats – one is already in its grasp – in Sabah, Borneo.

FROG MEAL The fringe-lipped bat of Central and South America uses hearing rather than echolocation to locate its prey, mainly frogs.

prodigious amounts of ammonia gas, which poisons the air. The ammonia concentration builds each year to levels that would be lethal to human beings but which are tolerated by the bats due to a complex physiological adaptation that allows them to lower their respiratory rate. By reducing respiration, the bats build up carbon dioxide in their blood and lungs in direct proportion to the amount of ammonia in the cave air. This carbon dioxide partially neutralises the ammonia and thus saves the bats from being lethally poisoned.

Deer Cave bats

In Sarawak, Malaysia, there are several large caves that are home to vast colonies of microbats. The largest of these is Deer Cave in Mulu National Park, which at 1.6 km long, 100 m wide and 120 m high, is the largest single cave passage discovered so far on Earth. The bats in these caves belong to several different species, the most numerous being wrinkle-lipped bats. The bats share their home with cave swiftlets, which return to their nests at dusk, just as the bats are leaving. At dawn, the bats return and the swiftlets leave. Significant numbers of straggler bats are picked off each day by peregrine falcons and a specialised bat-capturing bird of prey, the bat hawk. These dive down on the incoming or outgoing streams of bats and consume them in flight. An additional hazard for both bats and swiftlets are cave racer snakes, which dangle from stalactites and grab the birds and flying mammals as they negotiate the narrower cave passages.

As in Bracken Cave, the guano on the floor of Deer Cave is home to a complex community of organisms, including seething masses of golden cave cockroaches, cave earwigs, beetles and other insects that feed on guano and the bats and swiftlets that occasionally fall to the floor. These insects, in turn, provide food for other invertebrates – centipedes and spiders, some as big as a hand, others that hide deep in white tunnel webs within the darker recesses of the cave.

Bat guano also contains billions of bacteria belonging to numerous different species. In recent years, scientists have identified substances made by these bacteria that have actual or potential uses in detoxifying industrial waste, producing antibiotics and insecticides, improving detergents and converting waste by-products into alcohol. Bat colonies are beneficial to humans in more ways than one.

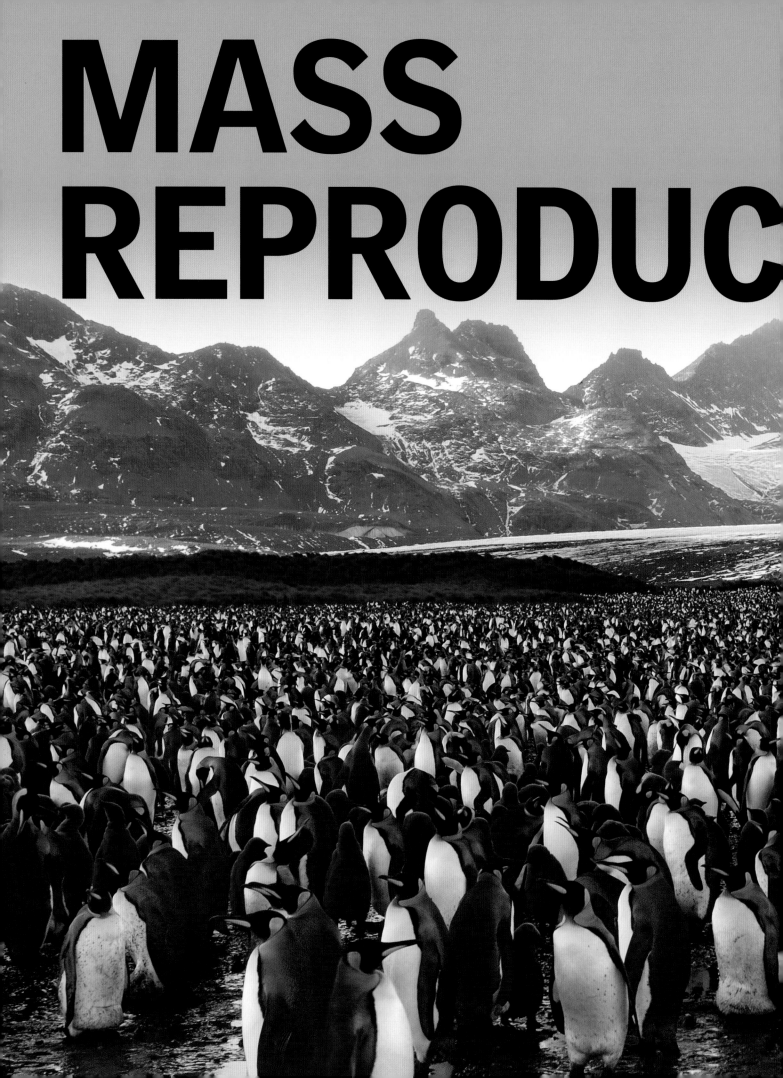

MASS
REPRODUC

TION 3

A BREEDING COLONY OF HALF A MILLION KING PENGUINS OCCUPIES A COASTAL PLAIN ON THE ISLAND OF SOUTH GEORGIA in the South Atlantic (left). For many animals, congregating in large numbers to breed is a response to the pressures of sexual selection. It allows female animals, who focus on biological fitness when selecting potential mates, to choose among many males. For males, who concentrate on finding the greatest number of sexual partners, it means that the best adapted can mate with numerous females. Either way, the animals improve the chances that their genes will carry on into future generations. At the same time, having vast numbers of offspring ensures that at least some will survive, while synchronised breeding can reduce the effects of predation by satiating the appetites of the predators.

PULLING POWER

FOR THE MALES OF MANY SPECIES, THE MATING SEASON BRINGS A HECTIC ROUND OF COMPETITIVE MATING DISPLAY. This involves various forms of extravagant behaviour, such as displaying brightly coloured plumage, performing dances or gymnastic exhibitions, or producing loud vocalisations, including honking or booming sounds. The males of species such as grouse and some bats arrange themselves into neighbouring territories, where they 'strut their stuff' in the hope of attracting females to mate with them. The displays and the territories in which they take place are called 'leks' (probably from an Old Norse word, *leka*, meaning 'play').

Laws of the lek

The females visit leks to assess potential mates, judging the desirability of the males from the extravagance of their displays. It is part of a process called 'ornamental sexual selection', most common among birds, although it also occurs in some fish and mammal species. If the females in a population are attracted to males with a particular trait or behaviour, that trait becomes a measure of a male's biological fitness. Males that exhibit it in a high degree are more likely to reproduce, and over time the trait is likely to become more pronounced in the population.

During the mating season, the leks assemble on a daily basis. The same group of males meets at the same place every day and takes up identical positions. Zoologists have identified two main types of lek. In 'classical' leks, the males gather within sight of each other and often tussle with their neighbours as each defends his patch of ground or water. In 'exploded' leks, the participants are more widely spaced and interactions among them are restricted to vocal signalling.

Within each lek, a ranking system usually becomes established. The males with the most 'pulling power' take the most prestigious central territories, while subsidiary males arrange themselves around the periphery. As females arrive, they normally gravitate towards one or other of the males in the centre. As a result, this dominant minority ends up mating with the majority of the females. Once mated, the females go elsewhere to lay their eggs or complete gestation.

Various hypotheses exist about how lek formation evolved. From the female point of view, the advantages are clear: the

MOORLAND LEK Three male black grouse at a lek in the Scottish Highlands flaunt their tails in hope of attracting a female.

THROAT DISPLAY Male frigate birds show off their bright red throat patches as they cluster together in a lek in the Galápagos Islands.

grouping of aspirant males in leks allows females to choose desirable mates with the minimum of energy expenditure and reduced risk of predation. For males – particularly the less dominant ones – the benefits are less obvious, except that leks tend to attract more females than dispersed males would. The bigger the lek, the more females are attracted, which means that even less dominant males are more likely to mate successfully. A simpler explanation is that males form clusters in areas where females are most likely to be encountered – for example, where food is most abundant or where female home ranges overlap.

Lekking is particularly common among ground-dwelling birds. In North America, sage grouse puff up their ruffled white breasts to reveal two yellowish air sacs, which they rapidly inflate and deflate, producing a popping sound. A related species, prairie chickens, have similar gold or red neck sacs which they puff up, making a booming sound. In northern Europe, black grouse strut around with their tails spread and heads held low, making their distinctive mating calls. In Asia, peacocks show off their tails. In both black grouse and peacocks, leks are composed of brothers and half-brothers, so the lower-ranking males help to propagate their own genes by attracting mates for their brothers.

In lakes in Malawi, Mozambique and Tanzania, lekking can be seen among the males of freshwater cichlid fish, who build underwater sandcastles to impress the opposite sex. The male with the tallest mound of sand, which can be almost 1 m wide at the base, wins the most females. A few antelopes also engage in leks, including the Ugandan kob. Kob leks contain anything between 12 and 200 males, each occupying his own circular territory, with fierce competition for the innermost territories.

Elsewhere in Africa, male hammer-headed bats line up on riverbank tree branches at night, at intervals of about 10 m. At dusk and dawn, the bats advertise themselves by rapid wing flapping, accompanied by honking and croaking. Females fly along the river assessing the males. Once a female has made her choice, she lands on the branch beside the male and mating ensues. There is a high variation in male success: researchers observed that in one bat lek 6 per cent of the males took part in 79 per cent of the matings.

SLIVERS OF SILVER Male and female capelin (left) form a squirming silvery mass as they intertwine on a Newfoundland beach. This mass spawning ritual happens every year. Capelin are semelparous – they breed only once in their lifetimes.

NIGHT-TIME SPAWNING Star coral (below) releases spawn into the darkened waters of Flower Garden Banks National Marine Sanctuary in the Gulf of Mexico.

SYNCHRONISED BREEDING

EVERY YEAR, FOR A FEW DAYS IN LATE JUNE AND EARLY JULY, MILLIONS OF SMALL SILVERY FISH CALLED CAPELIN CONVERGE off the beaches of Newfoundland and Labrador in eastern Canada. Here, the females broadcast their eggs and the males their milt (fish sperm) in the shallow sandy or gravel-bottomed water. About 15 days later, billions of fertilised eggs hatch into vast throngs of larvae. The parent fish are mostly three to four years old, and it is the only time in their lives that they will spawn. Following the mass spawning, most of the males and some females die and roll onshore in the surf, where local people collect them in nets or buckets. Thousands of seabirds also gather in the certainty of easy pickings for a quick meal.

Swamped appetites

Synchronised breeding has a number of advantages for the various marine species that practise it. For the capelin, it is partly a means of coping with the effects of predation. By spawning together, the fish ensure that their larvae all hatch within a short period of time, swamping the feeding capacity of predators, which include bigger fish, such as cod and herring. With the predators' appetites satiated, at least some of the capelin larvae will survive to become adult fish.

Mass spawning brings similar benefits to the various salmon species. After growing up at sea, all salmon return to breed in the same rivers in which they hatched, each of which has its own olfactory signature – detectable by the fish's sense of smell. Guided by this, the salmon travel up their home rivers to their spawning grounds, where within a few weeks of spawning they die. Awaiting their return is a seemingly devastating array of predators. For species such as the sockeye and chinook salmon coming back to Alaskan rivers, this ranges from salmon sharks and Steller sea lions – which intercept the fish as they head for the estuaries – to ospreys and eagles circling overhead and grizzly bears ambushing them at rapids and waterfalls. By arriving at their rivers en masse, the salmon maximise the chances that enough of them will make it through to the spawning grounds.

Sea-borne sex

For another group of synchronised breeders, mass spawning allows sexual reproduction to occur. In precisely timed mass-spawning events each year, most of the large reef-building coral species release millions of gametes (sex cells) into the sea. Because adult corals are fixed in place, individual colonies – which consist of many genetically identical animals, called polyps – cannot move into reproductive contact with each other. Releasing their gametes into the water means that the gametes have some prospect of meeting eggs or sperm from other colonies of the same species. To maximise the chances of this happening, the sex cells have to be released in a precisely synchronised manner and in extremely large numbers.

Exactly how this happens varies. About a quarter of reef-building coral species form what are termed gonochoristic colonies, each of which produces either eggs or sperm, but not both. The remaining three-quarters are hermaphroditic, which means that they produce both eggs and sperm. While gonochoristic corals discharge streams of either sperm or eggs, the hermaphroditic corals release small packages or blobs, often coloured pink or orange, which contain a mixture of both sperm and eggs. Billions of these spawn packages rise to the surface, forming oily slicks, which may be several metres long. Once on the surface, the packages burst open, liberating eggs and sperm, which then seek out counterparts so that fertilisation can occur.

Within days of sperm and eggs meeting, countless free-swimming coral larvae develop which, in the grasp of tides and currents, embark on voyages that can last from a few days to months and may carry them hundreds of miles from where they were originally released. If the tiny animals survive the ever-hungry mouths of filter feeders and plankton scavengers, they may eventually settle on a hard surface and begin producing calcium carbonate skeletons – thus generating a new generation of coral reefs.

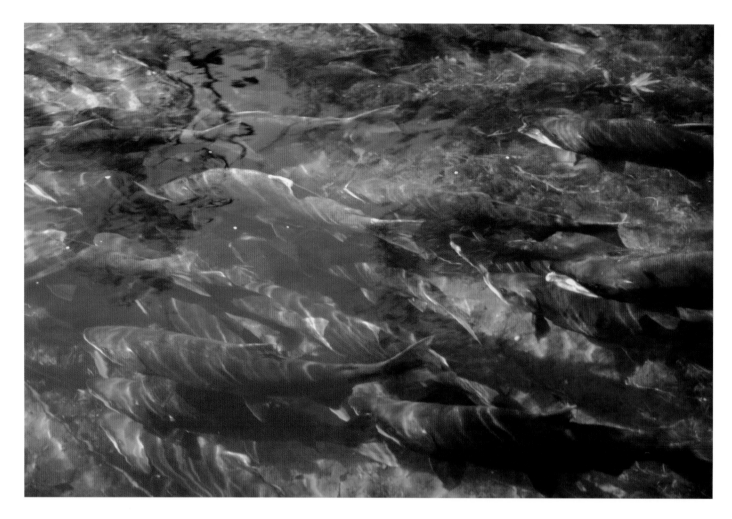

SALMON RUN Brightly coloured sockeye salmon swim up the Adams River in British Columbia to spawn. Millions of them converge on the river for three weeks every October.

Triggers for spawning

A variety of cues trigger mass-spawning events, from the waxing and waning of the Moon and tidal cycles to other environmental factors, such as changes in food abundance or the temperature or salinity of the water. For corals, the triggers are not clear, but they may be linked to changes in water temperature along with tidal cycles and daily variations in light levels. Corals in the reefs of Palau in the tropical western Pacific usually spawn a few days after the Full Moon in April. In Australia's Great Barrier Reef, mass spawning takes place five nights after the November Full Moon; in the Gulf of Mexico, it happens on the eighth or ninth night after the August Full Moon. Coral spawning usually occurs a few hours after sunset.

In California, another mass spawning coincides with the high spring tides that come two to six nights after a Full or New Moon. The females of a slender sardine-sized fish called the grunion come in on the tides to sandy beaches, dig their tails into the sand and lay their eggs. At the same time, up to eight males attempt to mate with each female by curving around her and releasing their milt as she deposits her eggs about 10 cm below the sea's surface. The female twists free and returns to the ocean with the next wave. For the next 12 days or so, the fertilised grunion eggs remain hidden in the sand. Then at the next set of spring tides they hatch and the larvae are washed out to sea.

Also off California, a squid species called the market squid engages in regular mating orgies in which the animals swarm into shallow waters and grasp one another. After mating, the male squid

**LESS THAN 0.001 PER CENT OF THE FERTILISED EGGS OF** most oceanic fish species survive to become adults. This low survival rate is the result of predation and it illustrates the importance of mass spawning and synchronised breeding to satiate predators.

CORAL SPAWN coalesces in certain sea conditions to form vast slicks that are visible from space.

100 MILLION RED LAND CRABS ARE estimated to take part in the annual breeding march to the sea on Christmas Island.

OLIVE RIDLEY TURTLE

THOUSANDS OF OLIVE RIDLEY SEA TURTLES COME ASHORE EACH MONTH TO BREED ON THE BEACH OF PLAYA OSTIONAL ON COSTA RICA'S PACIFIC COAST.

Known locally as an 'arribada' – from the Spanish for 'arrival' – this spectacular example of synchronised breeding takes place at each high tide over a period of up to ten days, usually during the last quarter of the lunar cycle. During the wet season from May to December, as many as 300 000 female turtles may appear out of the sea in a single month.

The female turtles push themselves up the beach to about 50 m above the shoreline. Here, each one digs a nest about 40 cm deep and deposits a clutch of around 100 eggs. They then scoop sand over the eggs and return to the sea – the entire process having taken less than an hour. The nesting density is so high that newly arrived females often dig up previously laid eggs as they excavate a patch of beach for their own clutch (because these newly exposed eggs are liable to be taken by predators, it is legal for people to harvest and sell them during the first 36 hours after an arribada). Some 50 days later the hatchlings, each less than 4 cm long and weighing just 28 g, emerge from the remaining eggs and scuttle down to the sea. Although huge numbers are taken by predators, tens of thousands succeed in reaching the ocean to replenish the overall olive Ridley population.

VITAL STATISTICS

CLASS: Reptilia
ORDER: Testudines
SPECIES: *Lepidochelys olivacea*
DISTRIBUTION: Tropical parts of Pacific, Atlantic and Indian oceans
KEY FEATURES: One of the smaller sea turtles, weighing about 45 kg as an adult; it also breeds on beaches in Mexico and India

die, and the females deposit cylindrical capsules, each containing 180–300 fertilised eggs, on the seabed – then the females, too, die. Three to five weeks later, small juvenile squid hatch from the eggs. No one knows where they go after that, but about three years later they return to the same place to breed and die in their turn.

Farther north, along the coast of Canada and Alaska, millions of male herring turn the sea milky white every March and April as they release their milt around eggs previously spawned by females on beds of seaweed. Off Samoa, marine invertebrates called palolo worms grow special tail sections filled with sperm or eggs. On a particular night in October or November, these break away in unison from their parent worms and wriggle to the water surface, where they burst apart. The floating eggs are then fertilised by the sperm, restarting the worm's life cycle.

Time-aware crabs

Among crustaceans, a spectacular synchronised-breeding event takes place on Christmas Island in the Indian Ocean. At the end of October each year, huge numbers of red land crabs leave the forests and move towards the sea to breed. The males are the first to arrive on the seashore, where they fight for the best territories. The females follow, mate with the males and several weeks later are swollen with eggs, which they deposit in the sea. The eggs hatch on contact with the water, and a few weeks

FLIGHT OF RAYS A squadron of large manta rays swoops in for an easy meal of plankton and fish larvae following a mass coral spawning on a reef off West Maui in Hawaii.

later carpets of tiny crabs emerge from the sea and head for the forests to start their life on land.

In Cuba, land crabs embark on a similar migration. During the spring rains, male and female crabs mate in the forests. Subsequently, the females carry their eggs down to the sea, swamping 20 km of coastline for a few days and bringing road traffic to a halt. Once at the water's edge, the females shake their eggs into the sea, avoiding being swept away themselves by the waves, and then head back to the forests.

Among reptiles, large, coordinated groups of female Kemp's Ridley and olive Ridley sea turtles come ashore on beaches in Costa Rica, the USA, Mexico, India and elsewhere. They lay their eggs, and a few weeks later the baby sea turtles all hatch out at the same time and head for the sea. In the Amazon, the yellow-spotted river turtle and other turtle species time their nesting and egg-laying to coincide with the peak of the dry season, allowing the hatchlings to emerge before the river floods.

Crocodiles and alligators, including the Nile and estuarine crocodiles and the North American alligator, leave less to chance. Squawks from hatchlings summon their mothers to dig them out. The mothers then guard them until they can fend for themselves.

Predator windfalls

Synchronised breeding helps species to survive predation, but for the predators events from fish or coral spawning to the hatching of baby turtles still provide windfall opportunities. When cubera snapper and dog snapper fish spawn at Gladden Spit off the Belize Barrier Reef, whale sharks are there, ready to take advantage of the sudden abundance of easy-to-find food. Groups of the sharks can be seen swimming line abreast near the reef, skimming the surface. At Ningaloo Reef in Western Australia,

whale sharks appear two weeks after the corals on the reef have spawned, feeding not on the coral spawn but on the zooplankton and small fish that have fattened up by feasting on the spawn. Squadrons of manta rays also congregate near reefs soon after mass-spawning events. They arrive at night like stealth bombers, swooping in one after another and looping the loop as they feed.

In Hawaii, tiger sharks wait offshore to intercept green turtles on their way to breeding beaches, and in Costa Rica olive Ridley hatchlings face a barrage of predators on their journey across the beaches to the sea. Iguanas crush the tiny turtles in their powerful jaws; ghost crabs grab them by the flippers and drag them into their holes; frigate birds swoop down from the sky to snatch them. For the baby turtles that manage to reach the surf, blacktip reef sharks are there waiting for them.

MANY FROGS AND TOADS PRODUCE SEVERAL THOUSAND EGGS PER BREEDING FEMALE. They are 'explosive' breeders, who restrict their breeding to one or two short periods during the year. When they do mate, they produce prodigious numbers of eggs and, as a result, their populations can explode a few months after spawning as the tadpoles develop into a new generation of frogs and toads.

In the tropics, several anuran species – better known as frogs and toads – breed only during the short-lived rainy seasons when ponds appear, essential for the development of tadpoles. In temperate regions, many breed only during a few weeks in the spring in anticipation of a particular food source becoming available in the summer for their developing offspring. The huge numbers of eggs they produce are partly to compensate for the restricted breeding season and partly to satiate predators (see page 68).

Almost all anurans are external fertilisers, meaning that the transfer of sperm to eggs takes place outside the female body. Mating begins with the male grasping the female in a firm embrace, called 'amplexus'. As the female secretes her eggs, the male releases his sperm either directly onto the eggs or into the water around them in a mating session that can last several hours. In species that breed explosively, the males usually far outnumber the females at breeding sites, ensuring that every reproductive female quickly finds a mate. Consequently, there is intense competition among the males. While many vocalise using loud croaks, chirps or trills to attract a mate, most rely on physically jostling each other, so the sheer size and

TOAD TURMOIL A mêlée of male toads scramble over each other in a spawning pond as they try to reach the available females.

EXPLOSIVE BREEDERS

BREEDING FROGS A mass of eggs surrounds a male and female common frog in a mating embrace. Tadpoles hatch from fertilised eggs (inset, right) with external gills (bottom) that allow them to breathe underwater.

amphibians, snakes, birds and fish means that only about one in 400 of the original eggs survives to become an adult toad.

Common frogs, like common toads, are explosive breeders, who return annually to the sites where they were born, but there are differences in how they breed. Female frogs produce clumps rather than strings of eggs and normally do not release eggs if more than one male embraces them, so mating balls do not develop. Multiple fathering can still occur if other males embrace egg clumps laid by mating pairs, releasing sperm that fertilises any so-far unfertilised eggs.

In the humid forests of Costa Rica and Nicaragua, a tree frog called the parachuting red-eyed leaf frog is another explosive breeder. Frogs of this species mate only after heavy rainfall has produced temporary ponds on the forest

aggressiveness of a male can be an important factor in his mating success.

Common multipliers

A widespread explosive breeder in Europe is the common toad. Each spring, adult toads return to the ponds or other stretches of still water where they were born, resulting in huge numbers of them migrating along established routes. In some countries, concerned naturalists help them to cross roads safely at this time by carrying them across busy crossing points in buckets, and in places special tunnels have been constructed.

Once the male toads have arrived at the breeding sites, the competition among them is so intense that up to ten may try to mate simultaneously with a single female, forming a multiple amplexus, or mating ball. Some females are swamped or even drowned by the eager males. Each female produces a double string of eggs – numbering about 1500 eggs on average, but sometimes as many as 4000 – protected by jelly, which swells up in the water to protect the fragile embryos. Because of the system of toad mating, the sperm of many males is released over the eggs of one female, so multiple fathering of the egg strings probably occurs. The fertilised strings become wrapped around the underwater stems of aquatic plants, where within a few days the eggs develop into tadpoles. Predation by insects, other

floor. At these times, they form spectacular breeding gatherings on lianas (long-stemmed vines) overhanging the ponds. As a male clasps a female frog, she lays her fertilised eggs on a layer of moss covering the vine that they are on and then empties her bladder onto the eggs to keep them moist. When the tadpoles hatch, they wriggle free and drop into the water below.

When not breeding, the leaf frogs live in the tree canopy. After heavy rain, they have to gather quickly in their breeding sites to take advantage of the water, so they 'parachute' down from considerable heights, extending their limbs and spreading out the flaps of skin between their toes and fingers to brake their descent. After breeding, the return to the tree canopy is a slower affair, as they haul themselves up the lianas hand over hand.

FLIES GALORE

FLIES REALLY DO BREED LIKE FLIES. During the warmer months of the year, the common housefly can produce a new generation in less than 12 days. Its whitish eggs, which are laid in clusters of 75–100, hatch within 24 hours to produce tiny larvae or maggots. After a larval stage lasting four to six days and a pupal stage that may last as little as three days, a new adult housefly emerges. Within 36 hours a female is ready to mate.

An adult fly typically lives for 15–30 days, and a female can produce several batches of eggs over her lifetime, so in theory – given unlimited food supplies and no predators – a single pair of breeding flies could give rise to more than a billion billion offspring in five months. In practice, of course, houseflies do not have an unlimited supply of food and they are preyed upon by spiders, birds, amphibians and other insects, so their numbers remain fairly stable over the long term.

Clouds of insects

Like houseflies, mosquitoes are true flies – they possess a single pair of wings and belong to the insect order Diptera. The life cycles of both go through the same four stages – eggs, larvae, pupae and adults – and vary in length from 4 to 30 days. Unlike houseflies, mosquitoes often form large spring and summer swarms, because egg-laying and hatching take place in synchronised waves. The swarms consist of mating adults and are thought to be held together by the release of pheromones – chemical substances that influence the behaviour of other members of the same species. Because mosquitoes go through their larval and pupal stages in places such as ponds, water butts and other rain-filled containers, swarms generally develop several days after a period of rainy weather.

In Africa, spectacular swarms of lake or nkungu flies emerge from lakes Victoria and Malawi. One of the entomological wonders of the world, the swarms look like columns of dark smoke, visible over the lake surface from many miles away. The flies develop from lake-dwelling larvae, which live on the bottoms of the lakes, where they feed for many months on plankton at depths of 200 m. Triggered by cues connected to the lunar cycle, the larvae eventually form pupae, which rise up through

MOSQUITO CLOUD A swarm of mosquitoes dances close to a forest road in Keoladeo National Park, India. Swarms often follow rainy weather, but can also result from earlier drought, which reduces the populations of mosquito predators.

the water. Fish eat many of them on their way up, but the ones that make it to the top emerge in massive swarms of mating flies, pushed in whatever direction the wind is blowing.

For birds, the lake fly swarms make such an attractive feeding proposition that terns migrate from Europe to feast on them. In some lakeside communities, people collect the flies using baskets attached to long handles. They crush and boil them, and mould them into balls, which are dried in the Sun to eat later.

Another set of swarmers, the mayflies, are not true flies, but belong to a group of winged insects called the Palaeoptera, which also includes dragonflies. During their immature stage, when they are called naiads or nymphs, they usually live for one or two years in freshwater. The adults are short-lived, surviving from a few hours to a few days depending on the species, but in their brief existences they can form dense swarms when all the naiads in a population mature and hatch at once in spring or autumn. The most dramatic swarms form in mid-June over rivers in Hungary and Serbia, such as the Tisza and its tributary the Körös. While swarming, mayflies are everywhere, dancing around each other in large groups and resting on every available surface. Sparrows, wagtails, swallows and blackbirds eat their fill, while trout and other fish crowd to the river surface to pick off the insects. It is said that any fool can catch a fish during these interludes, which have been called 'duffer's fortnights'.

The sole purpose of an adult mayfly is to reproduce, and mating occurs in mid-air within the swarms. In most species, the males' front legs are unusually long, the better to grasp females with. Most of the other anatomical parts of the male mayfly – and many of the females' parts, apart from the egg-producing and egg-laying apparatus – are vestigial and useless.

INSECT HORDES Male long-tailed mayflies swarm on the surface of the Körös River in Hungary.

STICKING TOGETHER

TOWARDS THE END OF HER LIFE, A FEMALE BLUE-RINGED OCTOPUS LAYS A CLUTCH OF ABOUT 50 EGGS. She then holds them in her arms for six months, during which time she is unable to obtain food for herself. Shortly after the eggs hatch, the mother octopus dies – not, researchers have discovered, from starvation, but because she is genetically programmed to die at this stage in the reproductive cycle.

Having huge numbers of offspring is not the only way for an organism to propagate its genes into the next generation. An alternative is to put extra effort into helping offspring – usually fewer of them – to survive. For many animals, this focuses on protecting the young when they are still eggs or larvae. Another octopus, the female giant Pacific octopus, lays copious amounts of eggs – several thousand of them – and then watches over

MATERNAL CARE A blue-ringed octopus – her body the size of a golf ball – holds a clutch of tiny pale blue eggs in her arms.

them until they hatch. This takes four to six months, depending on water temperature, during which time she grooms the eggs, cleaning them by brushing away dirt and algae with her arms, and providing fresh oxygen by blowing water over them. The eggs hatch into baby octopuses, each about the size of a grain of rice, and then the mother usually dies. Only a handful of hatchlings survive for more than a few weeks after their mother's death, but without her care hardly any would survive even that far.

Piscine protectors

Most fish species broadcast their spawn and leave the fertilised eggs, larvae and juvenile fish to fend for themselves. But a few take some care of their young. Discus fish – freshwater cichlids, native to the Amazon Basin – produce a slimy but nutritious secretion through their skin, which their fry (young hatched fish) live off during the first few days of their free-swimming lives.

Some fish groups are mouth-brooders – they protect the fertilised eggs or fry by holding them in their mouths for several

MALE BIRTH A male lined sea horse in the process of 'giving birth' to batches of his fry. Fertilised eggs develop in the brood pouch at the base of his abdomen.

weeks, during which time the adults cannot feed. In African lakes, a female cichlid lays a nest of eggs; then when the eggs have been fertilised by a male, she scoops them into her mouth for protection.
In Lake Tanganyika, cuckoo catfish take advantage of this by infiltrating their own fertilised eggs into nests filled with unfertilised cichlid eggs. When the female cichlid takes her fertilised eggs into her mouth, cuckoo catfish eggs are mixed in with them. A few weeks later, the catfish eggs hatch and the baby catfish devour the cichlid eggs. With little or no expenditure of energy, the catfish has not only arranged protection for her eggs, but also procured a nutritious meal for her young when they are born.

In some fish species, such as the yellowhead jawfish – a colourful inhabitant of coral reefs in the Caribbean – and the Banggai cardinalfish, it is the male who mouth-broods the eggs. The male silver arowana fish of the Amazon goes one step further by mouth-brooding the eggs and later the fry during their first few weeks of life.

In sea horses – which despite appearances are species of fish – the fertilised eggs develop in a special brood sac on the male's abdomen. Production and fertilisation of the eggs comes at the end of an extended courtship ritual, which may include the male and female swimming side by side holding tails, or gripping the same strand of sea grass with their tails and wheeling around one another. Once the female's eggs have reached maturity, the sea horses begin their final mating session, which lasts for about eight hours. The male expands the brood pouch on his abdomen by pumping water into it. The male and female then drift upwards out of the sea grass, often spiralling as they rise. As they do so, the female inserts a tube into the male's pouch and squirts anything from a few dozen to a thousand eggs into it. At the same time, the male releases his sperm into the seawater, and this, too, makes its way into the pouch where it fertilises the eggs.

Both sea horses then sink back to the bottom and the female swims off – although she visits her partner over the following weeks, swimming over for a few minutes of interaction each day. The fertilised eggs, meanwhile, become embedded in the wall of the male's brood sac, surrounded by tissue. About two to three weeks later, tiny sea horses emerge. For a few more hours they stick together in the pouch, where the salinity of the water is carefully regulated, preparing them for life in the sea. Finally, the male sea horse releases the fry in batches into the seawater.

Other attentive fish fathers include male sand gobies, who guard nests of fertilised eggs until the young are born. But they seem to do this diligently only if females are also present. Without the females, the males sometimes eat the eggs. This suggests that their parental care is principally a tactic for

attracting mates. A female goby is sexually drawn to a male who is – outwardly at least – a conscientious nest guard. If she mates with him, he will improve the chances that her offspring will survive, with little energy expenditure by herself.

Family-oriented frogs

Several species of frog and toad provide out-of-the-ordinary parental care for their fertilised eggs. In the rain forests of Central and South America, a female poison-dart frog will lay clutches of 5–20 eggs on a smooth flat surface inside a male's territory. After fertilising them, the male tends the eggs, keeping them moist while they develop. When the tadpoles hatch, he allows them to attach themselves one at a time to his back, then moves them to a suitable patch of still water, such as a small pond, a wet hole in a tree stump or even a water-filled coconut shell, at which point he leaves them to fend for themselves.

The male Darwin's frog, found in forest streams in Chile and Argentina, fertilises clutches of 30 or so eggs laid by a female and guards them for about two weeks until they hatch. He then picks up the developing tadpoles and carries them around for several weeks in his vocal pouch. When the froglets have reached a length of about 1 cm, they hop out and swim away. The female Surinam toad, an aquatic South American species, provides even more personal care. Her fertilised eggs adhere themselves to her back, where they become embedded in pockets within the skin, producing an irregular 'honeycomb' appearance. They remain there, developing through the tadpole stage, until after 12–20 weeks, they have fully metamorphosed into 2 cm long toadlets. Eventually, picking a time when the mother is fully submerged, they pop out in quick succession through membranes covering the skin pockets and swim off to begin their independent existences.

Caring bugs and beetles

With the exception of colony-forming social insects, such as ants and bees, relatively few species of insect spend much time and energy caring for their young. Among ones that do, the majority are semelparous – one-time breeders. Because they have invested their entire genetic future in a single batch of offspring – 'putting all their eggs in one basket' – it pays them to guard that investment carefully.

EGG WATCH A male giant water bug keeps guard over a clutch of eggs. He also keeps the eggs moist by regularly dripping water onto them.

AN ARRAY OF LARVAE A female tortoise beetle in a Brazilian rain forest protects her symmetrically arranged brood of larvae by perching on top of them.

Among these insects, the mother usually does most or all of the work. In the forests of South America, female Brazilian tortoise beetles guard their offspring from the time they are eggs. A mother shepherds the hatchlings to food sources, taking care to round up stragglers, and when disturbed by predators, such as ants or a wasp, she stands on top of her closely packed brood of larvae to protect them from attack. The larvae also have a remarkable defence of their own. At the ends of their bodies, close to their anuses, they have tiny hooks with small lumps of faecal matter attached to them. When approached by a predator, the larvae wave the faecal pellets at the intruder in an unusual but effective riposte.

Several species of shield bug protect their young – the female European shield bug challenges clutch-raiding enemies by standing fast and tilting her body towards marauders. In East Africa, a species of praying mantis seeks out a laying site for her egg sac that will provide good camouflage. In addition, in case the camouflage fails, she stands sentry over the eggs until they hatch.

Some beetle species make special arrangements to ensure that their offspring are well fed. Female fungus beetles, which feed exclusively on fungi, herd their larvae from one patch of fungus to another, like a shepherd with sheep. Burying beetles seek out a carcass, such as that of a mouse or small bird, and bury it as a future source of food. The female lays her eggs nearby, and when larvae hatch from the eggs, they move into a pit the parents have created in the carcass. Although the larvae can feed themselves, the parents also digest flesh from the carcass and regurgitate it as a liquid feed.

Dedicated dads

One insect family in which the males look after the young is the giant water bugs. In some species, the female lays eggs on a stick protruding out of the water. The male repeatedly climbs onto the stick to drip water onto the eggs so that they remain moist; he also drives off predators. In other species, the female glues eggs onto the male's back. In this case, he has to keep floating to the water surface to expose the eggs to air.

In most insect species, a male cannot be certain that he is the father of a particular clutch of eggs or nymphs, which is one reason why male insects are generally uninterested in supporting their offspring. Typically, there is a delay between mating and egg-laying, so after a male has mated with a female there is a chance that one or more other males will also 'nip in' to mate with her before she lays her egg clutch. For purposes of propagating a male's genes, it is usually more cost-effective for him to concentrate on finding new mates. Where the male is an egg-carer, it is usually because he can be reasonably certain that he is the father – because the female laid the eggs immediately after mating, or even during mating.

This is the case with one species of assassin bug in which the male makes a great show of attention to newly laid eggs. Males of this species even fight over the right to guard egg clutches. But – as with male sand gobies – they may have an ulterior or extra motive. Observations have revealed that females refuse to mate with a male unless he has shown a previous commitment to a nurturing role by guarding an egg mass. The male's behaviour ultimately seems to be slanted more towards attracting females than caring for offspring.

Just as rare as insect male carers are insect species where both parents play nurturing roles. One instance is the parents of young passalid beetles. These cooperate to chew out galleries of interconnecting tunnels in rotting wood, producing a refuge in which their offspring can live and hide. They also care for their young by preparing food for them – finely chewed wood chips mixed with faeces. In addition, they help their larvae to construct individual pupal cases.

EVERY YEAR SEALS AND SEA LIONS COME TOGETHER IN HUGE NUMBERS TO BREED ON BEACHES OR ROCKY OUTCROPS ACROSS THE GLOBE. Containing as many as 15 000 animals, these 'seal rookeries' are noisy, boisterous places, consisting of a number of distinct, fiercely defended territories, each occupied by a single, large, musty-smelling male, called a 'beachmaster', and up to 80 females. On a typical day, the beachmasters will mate with several of the females and have frequent raucous fights or stand-offs with male neighbours. In addition, hundreds or thousands of baby seals bark out for their mothers, and an equal number of frisky non-breeding juveniles spar continuously with each other.

Three groups of pinniped, as seals and sea lions are officially known, form large colonies of this type: fur seals, sea lions and elephant seals. The rookeries are located on coasts and islands in the northern and eastern Pacific, the sub-Antarctic region, Argentina, south-western Africa, southern Australia and New Zealand. Most other seals – the 'true' or earless seals, such as common, harp and Weddell seals – do their courting and mating underwater, so do not need to form large breeding colonies on land.

ROOKERY AT REST Hundreds of mostly female Cape fur seals rest on a breeding beach at the Cape Cross Seal Reserve on Namibia's Skeleton Coast.

SEAL ROOKERIES

BEACHMASTERS Male Steller's sea lions with their females crowd together in a rookery on South Marble Island in Alaska's Glacier Bay National Park.

Rookery organisation

Altogether, 17 different species form rookeries, but these are all fairly uniform in their characteristics and organisation. The males, or bulls, lumber onto the beaches in mid-spring, ending migrations that may have taken them thousands of kilometres from their winter feeding areas. The peak mating season comes in mid-summer, and by mid-autumn all the pinnipeds have dispersed and the rookery beaches fall silent once more.

Once on the beaches in spring, the males battle for control of breeding territories – essential if they are going to attract and mate with breeding females when these arrive. Generally, there are far more bulls wanting to breed than available, adequately sized territories, and in the physical struggle to procure space on the beach, size and strength are paramount. As a result, sheer size has evolved as a sexually selected trait in the males, producing a remarkable difference in bulk between the two sexes. A male Antarctic fur seal weighs about 150 kg on average, whereas a female weighs 50 kg; a male northern elephant seal weighs up to 2.5 tonnes, a female about 700 kg. Bulls unable to acquire and maintain a territory gather in neighbouring 'haul-outs', making occasional attempts to displace the beachmasters from their areas of the beach.

Females of breeding age begin to arrive in late spring and early summer, followed by juveniles of both sexes. Many of the older females are pregnant from the last year's mating, and within a few days they give birth to their pups. Shortly afterwards, they are ready to mate. The amount of choice the females have in who they mate with varies. Among Southern Hemisphere fur seals and Steller's sea lions, breeding females can move around within a rookery and sometimes fight each other for positions in a particular bull's territory. Among elephant seals, most sea lions and the northern fur seal, there is little or no opportunity for females to move around and choose their mates. After taking control of an area of beach, a dominant bull will coerce females to move into his territory and stay there, forming a permanent 'harem'.

To complete a full season, a territory-controlling male may have to defend his part of the beach against neighbouring or marauding males for up to four months. This means that unlike the females – who can take trips into the sea for food and come back again to nurse their pups – he has no opportunity to eat. Over the course of the breeding season, a beachmaster may lose as much as a quarter of his body weight.

During the periods when large numbers of pinnipeds are arriving or leaving the rookeries, major predators stake out the beaches, notably great white sharks and orcas, or killer whales. Great white sharks frequent fur-seal rookeries around South Africa and New Zealand. They also lurk near beaches on the coasts of western Mexico and California, with rookeries of northern elephant seals and California sea lions. Orcas favour sub-Antarctic islands – such as the Kerguelen Islands, South Georgia, Macquarie Island and the Auckland Islands – which have rookeries of the southern elephant seal, Antarctic fur seal and New Zealand sea lion. Orcas also stake out rookeries of Steller's sea lions in south-eastern Alaska. They even sometimes propel themselves onto beaches to grab seal pups in their jaws.

FACTS

3 MILLION ANTARCTIC FUR SEALS AND MORE THAN 100 000 southern elephant seals breed on South Georgia in the South Atlantic each year. The island's breeding beaches include the largest seal rookeries on Earth and the world's densest gatherings of any kind of marine mammal.

HUNTING by humans between the 18th and 20th centuries brought some fur seal species close to extinction. Their numbers have since recovered.

DURING A SINGLE BREEDING SEASON a territory-controlling bull seal, the beachmaster, may mate with as many as 100 females.

FACTS

SEABIRD CITIES

COLONIES OF BREEDING SEABIRDS CAN BE IMMENSE, resembling human cities in the sheer numbers they contain and the volume of noise they generate. Some colonies consist almost exclusively of a single species. Others are home to several and because of their resemblance to the kaleidoscopic mix of peoples and cultures found in Middle Eastern markets, these are sometimes called seabird 'bazaars'.

The birds that make up these colonies come back each spring to mate, nest and rear their young. Hundreds or thousands of birds that normally forage far and wide over the ocean pack together on remote islands and coastal bluffs, many returning to the exact spots where they nested the previous year. In part, they

CORMORANT CITY King cormorants sit on their nests in a large single-species colony on Sea Lion Island in the Falklands. Each nest is perched on a mound built up over years from materials such as grasses and seaweed cemented together with droppings.

do this because they have exacting nesting requirements and suitable locations are relatively scarce. A good site must be within range of the seabirds' main food supply, offer specific nesting habitats and materials, and have few or no ground predators.

Whitened rock

In Scotland's Firth of Forth, Bass Rock is home to a few shags and guillemots for much of the year, but every spring and summer more than 100 000 northern gannets converge on it to nest. Seen from a distance, large parts of the island appear white from the sheer number of birds and their droppings, which are estimated to give off more than 150 000 kg of ammonia per year.

Other vast single-species colonies include the island of Juan de Nova in the Mozambique Channel between Madagascar and Africa, where more than 3 million seabirds, almost all of them sooty terns, breed between August and April each year. In the South Atlantic, the Falkland Islands have large single-species colonies of king cormorants, black-browed albatrosses, sooty shearwaters, southern giant petrels and five species of penguin

(see page 88). Isla Guafo off southern Chile is home to possibly the world's largest seabird colony with a summer breeding population of 4 million sooty shearwaters.

More common than single-species colonies are ones with many different species, arranged layer by layer according to their nesting preferences. These seabird cities provide some of the most amazing spectacles on Earth, with constant motion day and night. On the Isle of May, also in the Firth of Forth, the total summer population exceeds 200 000 seabirds and includes more than a dozen different breeding species. At peak breeding time in June, birds occupy every available nesting site – whether on the 50 m cliffs that girdle much of the island or across its rugged surface.

Each of the species on the Isle of May has its preferred habitat. Nesting close to the water at the base of the cliffs are common shags, which build their nests out of small sticks and strands of seaweed. Higher up, tens of thousands of razorbills and common guillemots lay their eggs directly on rocky ledges and tend them there. These ledges can get so crowded that birds returning from the sea may have to land on the heads of their

LEDGE NESTS Kittiwakes nest high up on a cliff on South Marble Island in Alaska's Glacier Bay. Inset: A kittiwake mother guards her chick.

colonies birds of different species also sometimes club together for the same purpose – gulls, terns and skuas have been observed cooperating to drive off foxes.

Terrestrial predators are not the only threat. Other seabirds, such as large gulls, also prey on the inhabitants of seabird cities and their young. A particular anti-predator behaviour in puffins is the so-called puffin 'wheel' – a large group of puffins flying in a wide circle over the sea just in front of their nesting grounds. As well as confusing predators, these wheels help to protect individual puffins from attack, since birds returning to or leaving a colony can join the wheel and then drop out near their burrow or on the sea. In some tropical colonies, huge spiralling columns of tropicbirds can be observed confusing frigate-bird predators in a similar way.

Colonies also act as food information centres. Throughout the day and night, continuous streams of birds are flying away from the colony in search of food, while others are returning. By observing the directions the birds return from, along with their behaviour after they come back – whether or not they have food to give their chicks – other birds can obtain clues about the likely location of food sources.

Sex and the city

In general, seabirds live longer than other birds, mate later and have fewer offspring – laying only one or two eggs per breeding season. At the beginning of each season, some time and energy are spent on forming pair bonds. Among guillemots, courtship rituals include bowing, billing (touching bills) and preening. Once a guillemot pair has formed, they usually remain together for the rest of the breeding season and often longer. All auks and gulls are monogamous for the season, with a high degree of mate fidelity from year to year. Some species, such as gannets, pair up for life, reuniting annually at the nest site, after spending the off season individually at sea.

Actual mating is brief. As with most other birds, male seabirds do not have phalluses; instead, after mounting a female, the male deposits a bag of sperm onto her external genital opening and the sperm then makes its way up into her genital tract. Once eggs have been laid, seabirds tend to invest more time and energy in their young than other bird species, the males and females sharing responsibility for guarding and incubating their eggs, then obtaining food and feeding the chicks. Albatrosses are an extreme example of this reproductive strategy. Some species breed only every two years or so, but spend many months raising their chicks, which may go on to live for 50 years or more.

companions. Ledges farther up are nesting sites for thousands of black-legged kittiwakes – dainty gulls whose 'kitt-ee-waayyk' calls are a major noise component of the colony. Above them are northern fulmars.

At the very top of the cliffs, tens of thousands of Atlantic puffins add a colourful contrast to the dark rock and green slopes, except when they disappear into abandoned rabbit burrows at night or during stormy weather. Other burrow inhabitants include storm petrels, which feed at sea by day and return at night to avoid predatory gulls. Finally, the flat moorland areas over the top of the island are nesting sites for lesser black-backed gulls, Arctic terns and great skuas.

City living

For seabirds, one of the principal advantages of 'city living' is protection against predators. Individuals of the same species can join together to mob and drive off intruders, and in mixed-species

GUILLEMOT ROCK Battered by a force eight gale, guillemots guard their eggs on Scotland's Isle of May. Inset: Brünnich's guillemots line up on a ledge on the Arctic island of Spitsbergen, where they form huge single-species breeding colonies.

PENGUIN ROOKERIES

PENGUINS ARE AMONG THE MOST SOCIABLE OF BIRDS, SPENDING A LARGE PROPORTION OF THEIR TIME WITH OTHER PENGUINS OF THE SAME SPECIES. They form groups to swim, travel, dive, feed – and, of course, breed. As with seals, groups of penguins that have come together to breed are called 'rookeries', varying in size from a few hundred to several million birds and nearly always containing just one species. Like seal rookeries,

penguin rookeries are noisy places, as adults squabble over nest sites, chicks call out for food and parents cry out to offspring that have strayed too far. The rookeries can also have an overpowering smell. Large amounts of guano (droppings) accumulate in the area, and it is often possible to smell a rookery long before seeing it.

Spring gatherings

Some penguin species living in warmer climates, such as the African penguin and Australia's little penguin, spend their whole lives in rookeries, since their young can be born and raised at any time of the year. Little penguins – the smallest penguin species, just 43 cm tall – even construct burrows in their rookeries. Among most other

penguins, the rookeries start forming in the middle of spring, as adults return to the same sites where they were born. Since all species, apart from the Galápagos penguin, live exclusively in the Southern Hemisphere, this means that the birds usually begin gathering in September or October – emperor penguins are an exception, congregating in April.

As with other seabird colonies, coming together in rookeries makes it easier for males and females to find partners and form bonds that will last for the rest of the breeding season. Courting males bow their heads and wave their wings to win the favours of the females, or in some species stand up straight with their wings held back while they make a loud wailing sound. The rookeries also offer protection against predators of eggs and

chicks, including skuas and caracaras (a kind of falcon), and a few mammals, such as stoats. A further advantage of colonies, applying particularly to emperor penguins who breed during the Antarctic winter, is that they allow the birds to huddle together for warmth (see page 56).

Nesting and hatching tend to be synchronised, with some variations among species. In most, the female lays two eggs in a nest made of piles of moss, grass, stones or mud. The parents cooperate in caring for the eggs, taking it in turns to incubate them; one sits on the nest, while the other goes to sea to feed. Emperor and king penguins – the two biggest species – are different from the others in that they lay just one egg per pair and do not build nests. After mating, the emperor parents separate for several months, the male staying with the egg while the female goes to sea. When the mother returns, they switch roles. Once the emperor chicks are born, they tend to huddle in large groups for safety and warmth. At this stage, the parents may go to sea simultaneously to find food, leaving a few 'babysitting' adults behind to guard the chicks. On returning to the shore, the emperor parents call to find their chicks in the mass of near-identical birds.

Spreading out

The largest penguin rookeries may cover an area of several square kilometres, always in coastal sites. Among sub-Antarctic species, chinstrap penguins gather on the steep, rock-covered slopes of islands such as South Georgia and Bouvet Island, while gentoo penguins assemble on ice-free cliffs and beaches in the Falklands Islands and elsewhere. Emperor penguins congregate on flat areas of sea ice near the coast of Antarctica.

Conflicts occasionally arise over matters such as male rivalry for a particular female, nesting sites and nesting materials. In any disagreement, penguins try to avoid a fight, using displays to warn each other off, such as staring at each other intently or slapping beaks together. If these tactics do not work, the adversaries may resort to fighting by lunging and pecking at each other. One source of conflict can arise when a mother penguins loses a chick, perhaps to a predator. She may attempt to steal another mother's chick, but these attempts usually fail, as other females assist the offended mother.

When breeding is over, most rookeries disperse into smaller groups, which will often spend the rest of the year together in the ocean. King penguins form groups of between 5 and 20 individuals that swim and feed together. In many species, the groups cooperate closely to catch prey. When Humboldt penguins locate a shoal of anchovies or other fish, the team members synchronise their dives, using head movements to signal to each other. They approach the shoal from all sides simultaneously, concentrating it into a tight ball. It is then quite straightforward to grab some prey by swimming straight through the ball.

SURF-RIDERS Rockhopper penguins propel themselves off the tops of waves to land on the shore. They breed in the Falkland Islands and on islands off southern Argentina and Chile.

REMOTE NESTING

ANIMALS WANTING TO GIVE THEIR OFFSPRING THE SAFEST POSSIBLE UPBRINGING will sometimes choose a highly unusual environment for breeding. In Africa's Eastern Rift Valley, millions of flamingos nest around one of the most inhospitable places on Earth – a remote lake in northern Tanzania, called Lake Natron, whose waters have a caustic chemical composition. The burning soda of the lake, together with extensive areas of hot, viscous mud surrounding it and soaring daytime air temperatures, make it a virtual no-go area for predators – and so relatively safe to bring up chicks.

Natron is so remote that its large breeding population of flamingos was only discovered in 1954. For many years, it has been the only regular East African breeding site for lesser flamingos – around 2 million of them – and an important breeding place for greater flamingos. Formerly a much larger body of freshwater, Lake Natron has taken on its present caustic state because of local climatic conditions. Consistently high temperatures, which often rise above 40°C, combine with strong winds to produce a high rate of evaporation. Water losses exceed inputs from rainfall and from various streams and hot salt-laden springs that flow into the lake at one end.

> **Lake Natron is by no means devoid of life. It supports large amounts of algae, particularly a type of blue-green alga called *Spirulina*, which provides the basis for a simple food chain.**

Despite these conditions, Natron is by no means devoid of life. It supports large amounts of algae, particularly a type of blue-green alga called *Spirulina*, which provides the basis for a simple food chain. The lesser flamingos use their beaks to filter the blue-green algae out of the water – a photosynthetic pigment made by the organism gives the birds their pink colour – while the greater flamingos feed on the larvae of crustaceans called copepods, which themselves feed on the algae. In addition, a species of fish, the white-lipped tilapia, thrives in the waters at the edges of the hot spring inlets. The only predators that can get through to Lake Natron are vultures and marabou storks.

Year-round nesting

Breeding for the lesser flamingos takes place throughout the year. It starts with spectacular courtship rituals, in which groups of birds march back and forth in step with one another, stretching their necks upwards and flapping their wings to flash the colours of their feathers. They then pair up to mate. Each pair builds a mud nest on the surrounding flats, which may be more than 25 cm high to protect it from flooding. A single chalky-white egg is laid and then incubated by both parents in 24-hour shifts for about 28 days. After hatching, the chicks are provided with food in regurgitated, liquid form for several months. They learn to run at one week, grow feathers at four weeks and fly at 12 weeks.

While the chicks require feeding, the adults often fly hundreds of miles on food-seeking missions. The major feeding sites are two other soda lakes – lakes Nakuru and Bogoria in Kenya – which are slightly less caustic and have a greater abundance of small crustaceans and blue-green algae. While the parents are

SITTING PRETTY Lesser and greater flamingos on nests made of salt-crusted mud near Lake Natron. The lesser flamingos have larger areas of black on their beaks.

away, the offspring gather in crèches up to 100 000 strong. Marshalled by adult birds, these undertake occasional walking treks of up to 30 km to drink at Natron's freshwater inlets.

Elsewhere in Africa, greater and lesser flamingos breed in northern Botswana's remote Makgadikgadi salt-pan complex, a huge system of salt pans that becomes flooded during the rainy season. In South America, three flamingo species – the Chilean, James' and Andean flamingos – raise their young in high-altitude salt lakes in the Andes, while the Caribbean flamingo breeds in brackish lagoons hidden amongst lava fields in the Galápagos Islands, as well as at various locations around the Caribbean.

COMMUNAL DENS AND NESTS

FOR AFRICA'S SPOTTED HYENAS, SOCIAL LIFE CENTRES AROUND A COMMUNAL DEN. Shared by up to ten females – the dominant sex in spotted hyenas – the den is a safe place where mothers can leave their offspring while engaged in other important activities, such as hunting. It is also where the young learn vital lessons about the strict dominance hierarchy, or 'pecking order', that prevails among hyena clans.

The use of communal dens, caves and lairs is widely distributed across the animal world, from spiny lobsters and hibernating snakes (see page 58) to mammals and birds. By sharing protected living quarters among several different families, animals can reap a number of benefits. Not only does a den or nest provide protection from predators and harsh weather conditions, it is also a place where responsibility for rearing offspring can be efficiently shared, while in species with complex social systems, such as the spotted hyena, it provides a nursery where the young can be socialised.

For spotted hyenas, life starts, in fact, away from the clan's communal den. Pregnant mothers typically drop their pups – usually two per litter – at the mouth of an abandoned aardvark burrow, in which the babies spend their first few weeks. During this time, pups of the

LOBSTER DEN A group of spiny lobsters – also called crayfish or rock lobsters – peer out from their communal cave off the coast of California. Within the cave, the lobsters constantly rearrange themselves according to rank.

same sex fight aggressively and many die. Then, two to six weeks after the birth, the mother transports the surviving pup or pups to the communal den. This becomes a young hyena's home for the first one to two years of its life, shared with other clan offspring of different ages. The communal den, another abandoned burrow made by a different species, is too small for the adult females themselves to live in, which is precisely what makes it a good place to leave the young. The small size of the entrance tunnel, along with the presence of older offspring who can still squeeze in, provides an effective defence against predators. The mothers visit regularly to feed their pups, summoning them to the den's entrance with whooping calls. Low-ranking females may be denied access to the feeding areas until more dominant mothers have left, which soon teaches juvenile hyenas about their own social status.

Cat and otter nurseries

Among mammals, feral domestic cats also nurse their offspring communally in dens – some of the largest are in Rome, where an estimated 300 000 feral cats have organised themselves into about 2000 colonies. In the Amazon region, giant otters dig 3 m deep communal lairs, or holts, in riverbanks. The otters live in family groups of three to eight animals, in which only one pair usually breeds, producing an average of four pups per year. As well as constructing holts, giant otters create common areas for playing, called 'campsites', where adults and young spend much of their time together when not hunting for food.

Birds that build communal nests include weavers, such as the white-billed buffalo-weaver and the sociable weaver (see page 94), the palmchat on the Caribbean island of Hispaniola and the monk parakeet from Argentina. Communal nests consist of several individual nest chambers, used by adult pairs to rear

HYENA TRIO A female spotted, or laughing, hyena relaxes with her two pups outside a communal den.

their broods. As well as providing defence against predators, the nests may also offer thermal protection against temperature extremes or structural protection against strong winds.

Another communal nesting arrangement is that of the ostrich. Each male ostrich has a dominant or principal mate, with whom he forms a pair bond, plus several secondary mates. All the hens lay their eggs in a communal nest – a simple pit about 50 cm deep, scraped in the ground by the male – but the male and dominant hen ensure that her eggs are kept at the centre of the nest. The eggs of the secondary mates are arranged around the periphery or even kicked out of the nest. Predators are more likely to consume the secondary eggs, so the dominant hen's eggs have a better chance of survival.

Other bird species breed cooperatively, with non-breeding birds, or 'helpers', providing breeding pairs with assistance – the helpers are usually closely related to the breeding pair. In Western Australia, pairs of red-winged fairy wrens hold territories for life, but share them with up to nine helpers – the female helpers assist in feeding the young, while male helpers expand the group's territory. Pairs with helpers show a greater success in rearing broods than those without. Young European bee-eaters, western bluebirds and Seychelles warblers that have failed to breed may also help close relatives with their breeding activities.

HOUSE GUESTS

CAPE COBRA

Together with the boomslang – a large-eyed, green tree snake – the small, slender and highly venomous Cape cobra is a good climber and one of the most frequent raiders of sociable weaver nests. In some areas snakes, including the Cape cobra, take an estimated 70 per cent of weaver eggs and chicks. Occasionally, a cobra or boomslang will curl up in a weaver nest chamber and make itself at home there.

SOCIABLE WEAVER

A highly gregarious species, sociable weavers create their individual nest chambers from dry grass, then weave them together into a communal structure, which they maintain throughout the year. Each chamber is round (up to 15 cm across), lined with fluff and reached along a 25 cm long tunnel. Spikes of straw surround the entrance hole to protect against predators. Adult weavers may raise four broods in a breeding season.

TAWNY EAGLE Along with various other species of eagle, owl and vulture, this large bird of prey will occasionally build its own nest on top of a sociable weaver communal nest. The weavers tolerate such 'house guests' because their presence deters other predators, and they normally do not attack either the weavers or the other small inhabitants of the community.

PYGMY FALCON This small raptor never builds its own nest. Instead, it takes over a chamber in a sociable weaver community. Because it feeds mostly on small reptiles and large insects, and may also deter snakes, the relationship between weavers and resident falcons is usually one of passive co-existence. On occasion, non-resident falcons prey on nestlings, in which case the adult weavers become highly agitated.

THE COMMUNAL NESTS OF SOCIABLE WEAVER BIRDS are the largest nests of any bird, sometimes weighing several tonnes. Found in the Kalahari and Namib deserts of southern Africa, they function like giant apartment blocks, with up to 300 individual chambers. They are occupied all year round, providing superb protection against the heat of the desert summer and the cold of winter nights. Not surprisingly, the nests attract a number of resident 'guests', such as pied barbets, ashy tits and rosy-faced lovebirds. A nest can survive for decades, until it becomes so heavy that it crashes to the ground.

COLONY

LIFE 4

BUSYING THEMSELVES AROUND AN ARRAY OF HONEYCOMBS, A COLONY OF WILD HONEYBEES IN A FLORIDA TREE engages in a multiplicity of tasks – extending their nest, making honey and feeding their larval brood. Highly organised colonies are common in the animal world, ranging from relatively small groups of mammals living in a maze of burrows to vast, marauding hordes of ants. Members of colonies are usually closely related and highly dependent on each other – group living reaches its extreme in some social insects that cannot survive singly. Colonies can persist for many times the lifespans of individuals and achieve impressive building feats. Structures such as termite mounds show how animals, by cooperating, can change their environment in ways that seem out of all proportion to the size and capabilities of individual members.

UNDERGROUND
COLONIES

MORE THAN 100 YEARS AGO, VAST NUMBERS OF COMPACT, CHIRPY LITTLE RODENTS OCCUPIED THE GREAT PLAINS OF NORTH AMERICA from southern Saskatchewan to northern Mexico. French explorers called these animals *petits chiens*, or little dogs, because of their yapping barks. They are now better known as prairie dogs.

The largest colony of prairie dogs ever recorded, in 1901, covered an area of about 65 000 km² in north-western Texas. It contained an estimated 400 million animals. No colony of that size exists today – they were destroyed long ago by ranchers convinced that the rodents were competing with cattle for food. But some sizeable populations are still found in protected areas, such as wildlife refuges and national parks.

A dog's life

Prairie dogs are short-tailed members of the squirrel family, closely related to ground squirrels, marmots and chipmunks. Adults have an average length of 38 cm and weigh about 1 kg. Their eyes and small ears are set far back on their heads. With short, muscular legs and strong claws, they are well equipped for burrowing and live in colonies of numerous closely spaced burrows. Their world is one of tunnels, which provide emergency escape routes in their deadly games of hide and seek with predators, as well as refuge from the sun and winter cold.

PRAIRIE-DOG CITY From their vantage points on top of the entrance mounds to their burrows, prairie dogs scan the surrounding flat terrain, as well as the sky, for danger.

Tunnelling requires considerable teamwork: front-line animals break through the soil, while a chain of workers shovel the soil through the tunnel system to surface openings.

A family group, or coterie, consists of a single dominant male, several breeding females and their offspring. Each coterie's burrow system has a network of entrance shafts and interconnecting tunnels that can extend for 30 m. Several coteries combine to make up a 'ward'. Coterie members are close knit. They recognise each other by smell and maintain their group identity through cooperative activities, such as digging burrows, raising their young, defending territory and grooming. Prairie dogs frequently make social visits with their relatives in nearby coteries and greet each other with what look like kisses.

Prairie dogs feed mainly on grasses and flowering plants. In summer, they eat voraciously to build up their stores of body fat for the winter, reducing the vegetation in their territories to just a few centimetres high. This creates open terrain, which promotes easier social contact between neighbouring coteries and helps the prairie dogs to spot approaching danger. Their predators include coyotes, bobcats, foxes, hawks and badgers. On spotting an enemy, a prairie dog announces the predator's presence to the coterie with a bark, then scurries down its burrow, where it listens to the movements of

FAMILY HOME The burrow system below would be occupied by a family, or coterie, of about five to eight prairie dogs. Dozens of burrows like this make up a colony. From the entrance mound, a vertical shaft descends for up to 5 m. Various passageways and chambers branch off the main shaft, including special rooms for sleeping, storing food and raising young. Some tunnels lead to additional exits. Should the whole burrow system flood, the plugged emergency exit provides a temporary air pocket and quick dig to freedom. Intruders such as rattlesnakes sometimes occupy abandoned chambers.

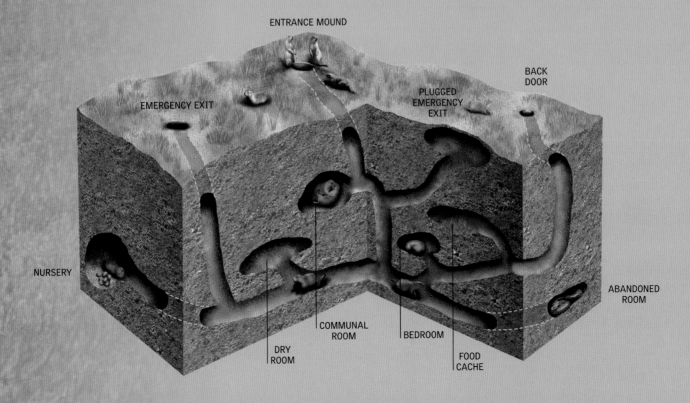

ENTRANCE MOUND

BACK DOOR

EMERGENCY EXIT

PLUGGED EMERGENCY EXIT

NURSERY

COMMUNAL ROOM

DRY ROOM

BEDROOM

FOOD CACHE

ABANDONED ROOM

the predator from a chamber near the entrance, coming out to give an 'all clear' call when the danger has passed. Prairie dogs also warn family members of trespassers from neighbouring wards by emitting a series of high-pitched yaps. The dominant male is extremely active in defence of his territory, constantly looking out for and challenging intruders.

Badger clans

Throughout much of Europe and Asia, the predominant tunnelling and colony-forming mammal is the Eurasian badger. Badgers form family groups, or clans, which can number up to about 30 animals but more often consist of 6 to 8. Each clan has a dominant male and female, which are often the only clan members to reproduce. The homestead occupied by a family of badgers, called a sett, is typically located in woodland. It is usually situated within sloping ground, and excavated in soil that is well drained and easy to dig, such as sand or chalk. It can consist of up to 300 m of tunnels, with 40 entrances and several chambers – though it would take several years and many generations of

BEDMAKING BADGERS A pair of badgers drag dried grass down into their sett to line a sleeping chamber.

badgers to dig a sett that size, and most are smaller and simpler. In cold regions, badgers dig down below the level at which the ground freezes, and all members of the clan sleep in the same chamber to share body heat. Sleeping chambers usually contain dried grass and leaves for bedding, which is regularly changed. Badgers deposit their dung in discrete corners of the sett complex.

Naked tunnellers

Like prairie dogs and badgers, naked mole rats are champion diggers of labyrinthine subterranean burrows, but they differ from their fellow tunnellers in that they spend almost their entire lives underground and in the dark. Their name is descriptive – they have no fur, they burrow like moles and have large front teeth like rats – but in fact they are more closely related to guinea pigs and porcupines. They live in arid conditions in East Africa, and their protruding teeth are essential for a life of

BURROWERS-TO-BE A group of naked baby mole rats display what will be their main digging apparatus – their incisor teeth.

excavating chambers and tunnels beneath the hard, sun-baked earth and gnawing the large plant roots and tubers that make up their diet.

Colonies of naked mole rats usually average 75 to 80 individuals, but occasionally number up to 300. They are unique in being the only known mammals to live in colonies presided over by a single reproductive female, called the queen. In this they resemble some social insects. Colonies also contain a few reproductive males, all the other members being workers under the control of pheromones released by the queen. Some mole rats work mainly as tunnellers, constantly expanding the maze of underground passages, and others mainly as defenders, protecting the group from predators. Should the queen or a breeding male die, a defender will become reproductive. A defender also occasionally sets off with an unrelated member of the opposite sex to start a new colony.

Naked mole rats usually breed once a year, and the queen produces a litter of 3 to 12 pups, though it may be as large as 25. The queen nurses the pups for the first month, after which other members of the colony look after them until they are old enough to obtain food on their own. As they have little hair or body fat, naked mole rats are hardly able to regulate their body temperature, and to stay warm they huddle together. They have also adopted some odd habits. They regularly roll around in excrement in their underground toilet chambers to refresh the smell of the colony on their bodies. This scent helps to establish who is family and who is an outsider when it comes to territorial disputes.

The excavations carried out by mole-rat tunnellers are aimed principally at getting access to roots and tubers. Colonies 'farm' tubers by eating part of them and then blocking off the tunnel temporarily to let them regenerate. Tunnelling requires considerable teamwork: front-line animals break through the soil, while a chain of workers shovel the soil through the tunnel system to surface openings. The last worker kicks the dirt up onto the ground above its head, where it forms a molehill. Because they have loose skin, mole rats can squirm past each other without getting stuck in the narrow tunnels.

Mobs of meerkats

Meerkats dig extensive networks of tunnels and sleeping chambers, which they can access via numerous entrances. The chambers are usually located about 2 m underground. Meerkat colonies, or mobs, contain around 20 members, consisting of a breeding pair and their brothers, sisters and offspring. The mob sleeps together for warmth in winter as they are particularly sensitive to cold. There are usually several sleeping chambers in each burrow system, but the mob only uses one at a time.

A mob's territory can extend over several square kilometres and contain many networks of burrows. The animals usually move between burrow systems every few days. One burrow is reserved for breeding, and when the alpha female gives birth, the whole mob will usually stay there for about three weeks – until the young are able to leave the burrow.

FIRST OUTING Two meerkat pups, escorted by an adult, venture out of the underground den for the first time.

ALL PULLING TOGETHER *These worker weaver ants (ten or so major workers and one minor worker) are cooperating to draw and bind leaves together to construct their nest.*

SOCIAL INSECTS

BY COMING TOGETHER IN VAST COLONIES TO COOPERATE OVER COMPLEX TASKS – such as constructing nests that are secure against extremes of temperature and weather, foraging for food and raising young – social insects demonstrate the true power of numbers. This way of life has enabled them to colonise and exploit hostile environments in which solitary individuals could not survive. Species that live in highly organised, complex societies, where all colony members work collectively towards a communal goal, are known by zoologists as truly social, or eusocial.

An important characteristic of social insect colonies is the existence of a marked division of labour – although thousands or millions of individuals live together, only a few are able to breed. These include one or more fertile females, or queens, which lay all the eggs and regulate the sex of offspring, and a few fertile males, or drones. Other colony members are sterile or near-sterile individuals, often females, and they carry out all the non-reproductive tasks required to keep the colony going. Two other characteristics found in eusocial insects are cooperative care of the young and an overlap in generations between parents and their offspring.

Social insects have been extraordinarily successful in evolutionary terms and include tens of thousands of species. The most familiar are ants, 3 groups of bees (the honeybees, bumblebees and stingless bees) and about 20 species of wasps, which are all members of the insect class Hymenoptera. Termites and some species of thrips and aphids are also truly social.

Reasons to be social

Social living provides many advantages, including a reduced risk of predation, more efficient food procurement and nest-building, and protection against environmental extremes. But what initially seems puzzling in social insects is the altruistic, self-sacrificing behaviour of the sterile members of the colony. According to accepted evolutionary theory, genes that improve their owners' chances of reproductive success should become more common in a population at the expense of genes that do not help their owners in this respect. So genes driving the types of self-sacrificing behaviour seen in the workers in insect colonies should quickly die out, as should the behaviour – but they do not. Even Charles Darwin was perplexed by the apparent paradox exhibited by social insects, referring to it as the 'one special difficulty, which at first appeared to me insuperable, and actually fatal to my theory'.

Darwin correctly anticipated that the resolution of this paradox would lie in the close family relationships between members of a colony. The behaviour of the sterile members of insect colonies is explained by a theory known as kin selection. This proposes that genes determining apparently altruistic or self-sacrificing behaviour persist in a population because the behaviour enhances the chances of reproductive success of related members.

Colony size and work-sharing

Many typical features of social insects are demonstrated by colonies of weaver ants, which live in sub-Saharan Africa, southern India, South-east Asia and Australia. These ants live in trees and are known for their nest-building prowess. A mature weaver-ant colony can hold 100 000 to 500 000 workers, span up to 12 trees and contain 150 nests. Workers come in two sizes, or castes – major workers, or soldiers, which are about 8–10 mm long, and minor workers, which are half that length. The major workers defend, maintain and expand the colony, forage for food and assist with the care of the queen ant; the minor workers tend the larvae.

Like most ant colonies, weaver colonies start off small, with just a few mated queens and the eggs they have laid. The first generation of workers construct new nests and help to rear the next brood laid by the queens. As the number of workers grows more nests are constructed, and as the colony's activity increases more complex coordination of worker activity becomes necessary. Communication works through pheromones (chemical messengers), tactile and visual signalling, and even brute force – workers sometimes seize other workers in their jaws and carry them to locations where more 'antpower' is needed.

Colonies of leafcutter ants, found in some of the warmer regions of Central and South America, can contain more than 8 million ants, mostly female workers. These ants cultivate a fungus in gardens within their nests, for which they need a continuous supply of freshly cut and chewed leaf fragments, which they use to compost the fungus. The worker ants are divided into several castes, depending on size. The smallest workers, with heads less than 1 mm wide, tend

PAPER NESTS Many wasps make nests from chewed-up wood fibre mixed with saliva. Paper wasps (left) build a single-layered comb of open cells. Median wasps (below) create a bulkier, multilayered nest with an exterior covering.

LIVING BRIDGE Foraging army ants use hooks on their feet to hold onto each other to form a temporary bridge along their route. Other ants climb over the ones forming the bridge.

FARMER ANTS The wispy white fungus that these leafcutter ants are tending is their sole food source. The ants cultivate the fungus in their nest.

to the growing brood of larvae or care for the fungus gardens. Somewhat larger colony members are generalised foragers, specialising in cutting leaves and bringing the leaf fragments back to the nest. The largest caste, called majors or soldiers, with heads about 7 mm wide, defend the nest from intruders. Ants of different castes share undertaking duties – removing dead ants from the nest or piling them up, on the equivalent of compost heaps, near the fungus gardens. Undertaking is a vital task in the nests of all social insects.

Army ants, which inhabit South and Central America, and driver ants, which are found from central Africa to tropical Asia, exist in colonies of up to 20 million individuals. Like weaver and leafcutter ants, the members of these colonies have different roles depending on size: the soldier caste have extra-large heads and pincer-like jaws. Bee and wasp colonies do not have a soldier caste, but there is division of labour among the workers. Depending on species, social bee colonies can vary in size from less than 50 (in some bumblebees) up to 100 000 or more. Colonies of social wasps vary in size from a few hundred up to about 5000 individuals.

New colony formation

Once a year, a queen ant lays some eggs that hatch into fertile males (drones) and young queens.

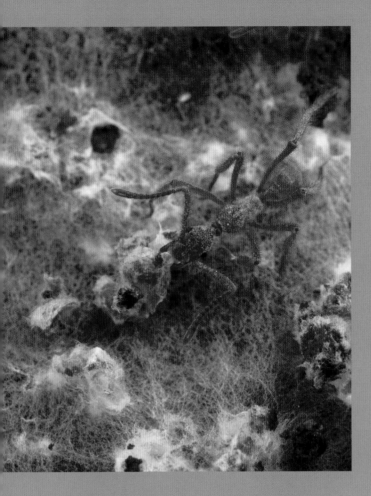

When fully grown, these ants have wings. They leave the colony in what is termed a nuptial flight, and the queens mate with drones from other colonies. The drones then die, and in some species the mated queens return to their own colonies. In other species, the queens fly off to start new colonies. On finding suitable sites they lose their wings and make small holes in the ground, then seal themselves in and start to lay eggs.

Some ant colonies are formed by splitting off from an existing colony, or budding. In army ants, only males have wings. They fly out from their parent colony in search of other colonies where virgin queens await. After mating has occurred, a colony containing one or more young, mated queens and an old queen then divides, each queen taking a share of the workers. When wood ants bud to form a new colony, the group of queens and workers who have moved away will sometimes remain in contact with the mother nest. If the new nest fails to flourish or is attacked, they can retreat to the safety of the mother nest, where they are welcomed back by their relatives. One species of tiny garden ant sends out 'house-hunting' scouts when establishing a new colony. When prospecting a potential new site, these scouts even measure up the

VORACIOUS EATERS These omnivorous army ants, native to Central and South America, are dismantling and consuming a fly that accidentally landed in their midst while they were feeding on fruit.

space available to be sure it is large enough. Once a site has been chosen, the scouts guide new recruits to it.

In social bees, virgin queens mate with winged males on nuptial flights, but in most species new colonies are formed by a mature queen leaving an existing colony. She takes a group of workers with her, in a phenomenon known as a swarm, while a new mated queen takes over the old colony. An exception to this pattern occurs in bumblebees, which start new colonies on their own after a period of hibernation (the remainder of the bumblebee colony dies off over the winter).

Nest construction

Social insects construct nests cooperatively, in a range of ingenious designs and from a variety of materials. Wasps make waterproof nests, often situated underground, using a papery substance that they make by chewing up fibres of dead wood and mixing this pulp with saliva. Ants build their nests in the ground, under stones or logs, or inside logs or hollow stems, using soil and plant matter. Some species, including the red wood ant, make large, conspicuous, dome-shaped nests up to 2 m across and 1 m in depth. They construct the nest from leaves, twigs and dry plant stems and cover it with a roof of conifer needles. This thatch keeps the colony warm in winter and cool in summer, enabling these species to colonise habitats with a wide range of temperatures.

Because army and driver ants are continuously on the move searching for new food sources, they need a way of creating temporary nests. The ants do this with their own bodies, gripping onto each other with their jaws and claws to form walls. These living structures represent the resting state of the colony rather than a nest, and so are sometimes referred to as bivouacs.

The most impressive of all ants' nests, requiring complex cooperative behaviour to construct, are those of weaver ants. In the first phase of construction, workers tug on the edges of leaves with their jaws to test the leaves' strength. If all is well, a

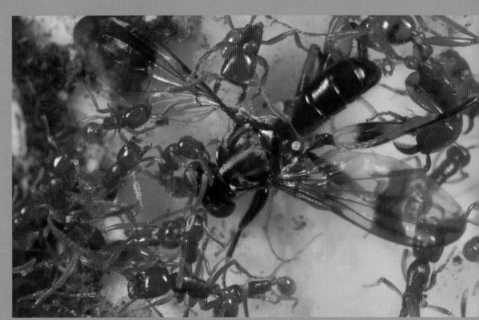

small insects or scavenge for dead ones to provide food for their larvae. Some wasps are omnivorous, feeding on a variety of fallen fruit, nectar and carrion; others sometimes invade honeybee nests to steal honey or larvae.

Ants forage for a wide range of food, depending on the species. Fire ants feed mostly on young plants, seeds and even crickets. They often attack and kill other insects, and even small lizards and rodents. Wood ants hunt long distances over the forest floor and climb tall trees in search of insect prey, while weaver ants also prey on small insects. Sahara desert ants forage for the corpses of insects and other arthropods that have succumbed to heat exhaustion. Running over the hot sand, they keep track of their position and navigate back to their nests by periodically noting their angle of movement relative to the Sun.

Army ants and driver ants feed mainly on other insects, but also eat larger animals such as lizards and snakes. When supplies become short, they form aggressive predatory foraging groups, known as 'raids', in which columns of up to 20 million ants move over the landscape in monstrous black tides, attacking prey en masse and consuming everything edible in their path. Sometimes they invade the nests of other social insects and steal their brood. Anything that is injured or immobilised – even a tethered goat – is liable to become trapped and consumed by the marauding ants.

Many ants keep insect livestock, such as aphids or scale insects, within or close to their nests. The ants herd the aphids or scale insects and protect them from predators and parasites. In return, the 'farmed' insects provide the ants with droplets of a sweet, carbohydrate-rich substance, called honeydew, which they secrete from their bodies. The ants stroke the insects with their antennae to make them secrete the liquid, a behaviour sometimes referred to as 'milking'.

Several ant species living in arid environments use the bodies of members of their own colonies as storage repositories for food, fat, water and other liquids to see the colony through the dry season. These 'living larders', known as honeypot ants, are kept deep underground, unable to move due to their bloated abdomens, which look like small, fluid-filled berries. Because of their high nutritional value and water content, these ants are a common target for raiders from other insect colonies.

few ants begin by bending a leaf in on itself or pulling the edges of two leaves together, then other workers join in. When the span between two leaves is too great for the reach of a single ant, the workers form chains by grabbing one another's waists. Multiple chains will sometimes work in unison to draw large leaves together. Other workers then fetch ant larvae and manipulate them to make them excrete silk, which is used to glue the leaves together. The largest of these nests are the size and shape of a rugby ball, and a colony will need to build enough to house all of its ants. Although weaver ants' nests are strong, the workers in large colonies continually build new nests to replace old, disintegrating ones.

Foraging and farming

With thousands – if not millions – of mouths to feed, foraging for food is one of the main tasks in an insect colony. Bees are specially adapted for foraging on plant nectar and pollen. Social wasps usually feed on nectar as adults, and may capture and kill

Slave-making

Some species of social ants have developed the tactic of getting other ant species to do their work for them. There are two methods used by these ants to enslave members of other species. The first is to carry out spectacular invasions of the nests of other species, capture eggs, larvae and pupae and carry them back to their own nest. There, the captured larvae develop into adults and act as workers for their new colony. Alternatively, a

HONEYBEES PLAY A VITAL ROLE IN POLLINATING

AGRICULTURAL CROPS AND ORCHARDS, which makes them the most useful insects known to man. There are seven species, but only one, the common or western honeybee (*Apis mellifera*), has been domesticated and spread all around the world. Honeybee colonies contain a queen, drones (males) and sterile female workers, which are normally all daughters of the queen. Colonies number around 40 000 to 80 000 bees in mid-summer. The nests consist of vertical combs made up of thousands of hexagonal cells in which the bees store their food (honey and pollen) and house their broods of larvae and pupae.

Worker honeybees have many tasks, which change over their lifetimes. For the first ten days they feed the larvae and build new honeycomb cells using beeswax secreted by glands on their abdomens. For the next week or so they receive the nectar collected by older workers and process it into honey, which they store in comb cells. They also receive and store pollen and may be involved in general hivekeeping duties. From about their 20th day, the workers leave the hive to forage for nectar and pollen. When a forager finds a new source, she performs a dance on the comb to indicate to others how far away it is and in which direction. Most workers die after a few weeks of foraging, but those born in autumn usually survive until spring.

The activities of a honeybee colony are controlled by pheromones released by the queen. Periodically, a queen needs to be replaced. If a hive becomes overfilled with honey, with no room for new eggs, this triggers a swarm in which the old queen flies off with about half the workers and a new queen takes over. A new queen may also be needed if the old queen dies, or if she weakens and her pheromonal activity decreases. When this happens, the colony kills her.

VITAL STATISTICS

CLASS: Insecta
ORDER: Hymenoptera
SPECIES: *Apis mellifera*
HABITAT: Well-vegetated areas containing flowering plants
DISTRIBUTION: Worldwide
KEY FEATURES: Workers produce wax and honey and have a venomous sting

HONEY BEE

108

SUNFLOWER GUARDIAN *A red wood ant drives off a seed-eating fly from an Aspen sunflower. In return, the ant receives nectar from the flower.*

slave-making queen will sneak into the colony of the other species, kill the queen and usurp her, mimicking the old queen by consuming pheromones from her body and releasing them to control the usurped queen's workers. Slave-making is surprisingly common among ants. A colony of 2000 slave-makers may have double that number of slaves. The slave ants forage for food, feed their hosts, tend the larvae and defend the colony against attack. If the colony moves to a new location the slaves carry their masters to the new home. Some slave-making species, known as Amazon ants, have become so dependent on slave workers that they are incapable of surviving for long without them.

Mutual relationships

Some ants have developed mutualistic (mutually beneficial) relationships with plants. Various ant species living in the Rocky Mountains have mutualistic relationships with a plant called the Aspen sunflower. The ants protect sunflowers of this species from flies whose larvae are seed predators. In return, the ants are supplied with nutritious nectar by the sunflowers.

In the tropical forests of South America there are 'super-nettles' that harbour ants. If something touches one of these plants, the ant inhabitants rush out to sting or bite the intruder. In Costa Rica, Azteca ants have a mutualistic relationship with Cecropia trees. The trees produce nutritious food bodies that are consumed by the ants. In return, the ants protect the trees from herbivores. The ants are extremely aggressive in protecting their trees, attacking any living organism that threatens them.

Some Australian ant species have a relationship with an uncommon epiphytic plant called an anthouse plant. The plant provides housing and food for the ants, while the ants protect the plant from predators such as worms. The plants possibly also derive nutrients from insect remains and other debris dumped by the ants. A third species plays a part in this relationship. The Apollo jewel butterfly lays a single egg on top of each anthouse plant. When the caterpillar emerges the ants carry it into their nest in the plant, where the caterpillar eats out chambers, providing the ants with increased living space.

Colonial defences

Social insects aggressively defend their colonies against attack using a variety of weapons, including venomous bites and stings. Many ant species bite and then spray the wound with formic acid, which has a paralysing action. Ants in particular have many potential predators, including other insects, spiders, birds, amphibians and anteaters. In ant colonies, soldier ants usually have responsibility for colony defence. Weaver ants are highly territorial, and even the lightest touch to one of their nests can bring the soldiers out in a fury. Although weaver ants lack a sting, they can inflict painful bites. Wood ants behave similarly, while fire ants bite only to get a grip and then sting, injecting a toxic venom called solenopsin. Fire-ant venom is both insecticidal and antibiotic: it is probable that fire-ant nurse workers spray their brood with it to protect them from microbes.

Japanese honeybees have an unusual method of dealing with any giant hornets that enter their colonies on scouting missions. Hundreds of honeybees surround the invader and they all vibrate their flight muscles. This mass vibration raises the temperature in the clump of bees to 47°C. The bees can tolerate this high temperature, but it is fatal to the hornet, which is suffocated in the heat.

Stings from social insects are a significant risk to humans, occasionally causing fatalities, although these are more often due to anaphylactic shock (an immune-system reaction) than to the direct toxic effect of the venom. Yellowjacket wasps sting repeatedly and aggressively if their nests are disturbed, and these attacks kill a number of people worldwide each year. Bulldog ants, found in Australia, are among the largest and most dangerous ants on Earth, well-known for their aggressive behaviour and powerful stings. One species, called the jack jumper, can cause death among sensitive individuals.

Communication

Insect colonies are large and complex organisations, with continuously changing needs. Sophisticated communication systems are required for the exchange of information – about food sources, for example, or to direct workers towards the tasks that they should be doing amid the multitude of tasks that need to be carried out. Most communication occurs through the release of pheromones.

Pheromones are chemicals that trigger a behavioural response in members of the same species, and are widely used in insect colonies. There are several types. When a member of an insect colony is attacked by a predator, it releases an alarm pheromone, which may trigger flight or aggression in other members of the same species. Sex pheromones indicate the availability of a female to mate, and are released by a queen bee or ant on her nuptial flight to attract males. Forager pheromones are released by older forager bees to slow the maturing of nurse bees in order to maintain the most beneficial ratio of nurse to forager bees. Trail pheromones, used particularly by some ant species, provide navigational guides to food sources.

ACID ATTACK A red wood ant prepares to spray formic acid from a gland in its abdomen. Acting together, wood ants can spray copious amounts of acid as far as 30 cm.

CASTLES OF CLAY

ODDLY SHAPED TOWERS OF DRIED SAND AND CLAY DOT THE LANDSCAPE IN WOODED SAVANNAH REGIONS OF AFRICA, AUSTRALIA AND SOUTH AMERICA. These impressive mounds are not just heaps of mud: they have an intricate internal architecture that includes chimneys, arches, tunnels and ventilation ducts. Deep within the mounds are specialised chambers for growing and storing food and caring for young, as well as systems for water collection and air conditioning. These castles made of clay are constructed cooperatively by millions of highly industrious worker termites.

Termites live in colonies that can number anything from a few hundred to several million individuals. The colony members are divided into several castes, including sterile, wingless worker and soldier castes, and a reproductive caste of males and females. Although usually blind, worker termites perform tasks such as nest construction, food gathering and care of the young. In some species, they also assist in the defence of the colony.

Nests and mounds

Termites use a combination of soil, chewed wood, saliva and faeces to create their elaborate nests, and workers have microbes in their guts that help to digest the cellulose in wood and plants. They build nests in many locations, some types living

SCULPTED MOUND The mounds of the West African savannah termite, Cubitermes severus, *are about 4 m high. The shape may protect the nest from heavy rainfall. Forest termite workers tend to the larvae in the nest's underground chambers (inset).*

TERMITE FISHING Chimpanzees poke long stems into holes in a termite mound. Soldier termites bite and grasp the stems, which the chimps then withdraw for a tasty snack.

in trees or man-made wooden structures, while others tunnel underground. The most spectacular nests are those built by subterranean termites. The core chambers are about a metre underground, and the termites use the excavated soil to create some form of mound above. The soil is cemented together with the insects' saliva and excreta to produce a finish as hard as concrete. To get water, termites dig down to underground springs or even to the water table.

Some African termite species construct mounds up to 9 m high, but the majority are about 2–3 m high. Shapes range from fluted cylinders and wedges to rough spheres or cones, while some nests consist of several small domes or cones piled on top of one another. The shapes are probably dictated by local weather conditions: nests in breezy areas have external buttresses to catch the wind, while piles of cones, seen in tropical West Africa, shed heavy rain.

So-called magnetic termites – leaf-litter-eating termites from Australia's Northern Territory – position their wedge-shaped nests to minimise the effects of the midday Sun. The mounds' broad flanks face east and west, towards the morning and afternoon Sun, respectively. This orientation has been shown to help control temperature. During the morning, the east-facing side of the mound warms up and many of the termites migrate to the west side to keep cool. In the afternoon, the reverse happens. At midday, the hottest time, only the thin upper edge of the mound directly faces the Sun, minimising the amount of heat absorbed by the nest.

Termites have an extraordinary ability to regulate the internal environments of their homes. To survive and thrive, they need to keep the temperature and humidity inside the nest at reasonably constant levels, and also flush out carbon dioxide and replace it with oxygen. They achieve this by building extensive networks of ducts and channels that control temperature and humidity and provide air conditioning. Such systems are at their most sophisticated in species that practise fungiculture.

Fungus gardens are located at the base of the mounds, nourished by the insects' excrement. The fungus must be kept at exactly 30°C and humidity at 100 per cent, even though temperatures outside can range from 1°C to 40°C. Through a system of carefully adjusted convection currents, air from outside is sucked in at the base of the mound and down into mud-walled underground enclosures where the fungus grows.

Warm air from the underground chambers rises through a channel to the peak of the mound. The termites constantly dig new vents and plug existing ones throughout the mound to regulate the temperature over the course of the day. No other creatures except humans are known to engineer their environment to this level.

Squatters and intruders

Perhaps not surprisingly, in view of the in-built temperature control and air-conditioning systems, termite mounds attract other residents. Lace monitor lizards in Australasia like to lay their eggs in termite mounds, while sacred kingfishers and hooded parrots make their nests in them. In Africa, dwarf mongooses commonly make their dens in termite mounds – very conveniently for them, as termites are their favourite food.

FACTS

THE LARGEST DIAMOND MINE IN THE WORLD WAS

discovered in Botswana thanks to the work of termites. When termites dig for water deep beneath their nests, they bring up every particle of soil and rock and add it to the mound. Specks of diamonds, gold and other precious materials indicate the possibility of reserves below.

400 KG of

termites are estimated to exist for every human being on Earth.

THE TALLEST TERMITE MOUND

ever found was 12.8 m high with a base 3 m across.

FACTS

OF ALL SOCIAL ANIMALS, BEAVERS ARE SECOND ONLY TO HUMANS IN THE EFFECTS THAT THEY CAN HAVE ON A LANDSCAPE. By building dams across woodland streams, beavers create small, tree-lined ponds and lakes. Eventually, if beavers remain in an area for long enough and continue dam-building, a swamp-like wetland develops. Over the longer term, when the lakes fill up with detritus and silt and the beavers move on, what was woodland may turn into an extensive habitat of fertile meadows.

Dams are not the only structures that beavers create. They also construct homes, called lodges, in and on the banks of the lakes they have created. Beavers are stronger and more agile swimmers than their principal predators, which include wolves, bears and wolverines, and their dams produce the aquatic environment in which they survive best. As their lakes become larger and deeper over time, the water not only

BUSY BEAVERS

BEAVERS AT WORK An American beaver felling a tree (above). An ongoing supply of wood is needed to maintain beaver lodges and dams (right).

provides them with safety, it also gives them easy access to an ever-increasing number of trees – their main building material – along the extending shoreline. In addition, the water provides a convenient medium for transporting logs and branches from the shoreline to the beavers' construction sites (dams and lodges) where they will be used.

Beaver families

Growing to over a metre in length, beavers are among the world's largest rodents. They reach this size mainly on a diet of grasses and aquatic plants. They are highly social animals. Their colonies typically comprise three or four families, with each family group consisting of the parents (who bond for life) and some four to six juveniles. Each family marks the boundaries of its territory with scent mounds composed of mud, faeces and castoreum (a strongly smelling oily secretion made by both male and female beavers), and works together to construct and repair dams and lodges and to collect and store food for winter.

Social grooming and play help to maintain the family bonds, as does sentinel behaviour. The usual warning signal given by a swimming beaver when it spots a predator is to smack the water forcefully with its broad tail and then dive. This creates a loud slapping sound that is audible over long distances both above and below water. On hearing this signal, nearby beavers dive and may not re-emerge for several minutes.

Dam and lodge building

Beavers build dams and lodges with considerable engineering skill. Working mainly at dawn and dusk, they transport large branches, mud and stones between their forepaws and smaller pieces of wood between their teeth. To build a dam they dump branches and small logs into the stream, then fill in the spaces between the branches with grass and mud. They may also use rocks, pebbles, mussel shells and other objects to strengthen the structure. Eventually, water begins to pool on the upstream side, and as this enlarges the beavers continually expand and reinforce the dam with additional branches, which they tow in from the lake edges. Once complete, the dams are strong enough for humans to walk across. In weak-flowing streams, they build dams straight across; in stronger currents, they construct curved dams to add strength, with the convex side pointing upstream.

Beavers can build immense dams: the largest ever documented was approximately 850 m in length, spotted in northern Alberta in 2007 using satellite imaging technology.

They are stimulated to build dams by any prolonged exposure to the sound of running water – they will even pile wood close to a loudspeaker emitting this sound. They continue to build a dam higher, and repair any damage, as long as the sound continues.

Beavers start working on their lodges in autumn. Lodges are usually cone shaped with underwater entrances and dens above the waterline. Beavers build from the inside out using branches, mud and grass. They generally construct two dens within the lodge, one for drying off after exiting the water, and another, drier one where family members spend the majority of their resting time. They cover the lodges with fresh mud, which freezes when the frost sets in, making it as hard as stone. The combination of piled-up branches and hardened mud on the exterior of the lodge – with the only accessible entrances being underwater – provides effective protection against predators.

Destructive and constructive effects

To obtain wood, beavers need to fell trees, which they are well equipped to do. They have long, sharp incisor teeth, which would grow at a rate of about 1.5 cm a week if not continually used to gnaw wood. These teeth are so strong that beavers can chew through treetrunks up to 20 cm thick . On average a family of beavers may fell 1000 trees each year. Although considered a pest in some places because of the tree damage and occasional flooding that they cause, the destructive aspect is usually outweighed by the environmental benefits beavers can bring. They encourage the development of wetland habitats, which provide homes for many species, and can increase a region's biodiversity. Beavers also assist in the provision of clean, unpolluted water as their dams filter out silt, and the associated wetlands help the breakdown of toxins such as pesticides.

GROUP
COMMUNICA

5

TION

THE CHORUS HOWLS OF GREY WOLVES RESONATE THROUGH SNOW-BOUND FOREST. They are using their voices to communicate – perhaps to contact a lost member of the pack, to celebrate a successful hunt, or to warn other wolves away from their territory. Vocal communication is also used extensively for signalling between individual animals and groups in the underwater world, notably by whales and dolphins, but also by spiny lobsters and many species of fish. Other, non-sonic ways of sending messages include scent-marking and varied facial expressions, gestures and other body language to express dominance or submission, plus a range of emotions from anger to friendliness. Among many species of birds and fish, highly organised schooling and flocking behaviour is made possible through precise communication by means of visual cues.

WOLF SPEAK

THE EERIE SILENCE OF A FOREST AT TWILIGHT IS PIERCED BY THE HOWL OF A WOLF CALLING TO OTHER MEMBERS OF ITS PACK. Vocal communication is just one of a number of ways that wolves send messages to each other. They also use a complex system of body language in order to express their relative ranks. Each pack has a highest ranked or dominant pair, called the alpha male and female, which are usually the only breeding animals. The other pack members are ranked below the alpha pair, and each knows exactly where it stands in the pecking order. The offspring of the alpha pair, for example, which usually make up most of the rest of a pack, are normally ranked in descending order of age.

When two wolves meet, the higher-ranked or dominant wolf stands up tall, with its tail raised almost vertically and ears pointing up. It looks directly (and usually down) at the other wolf. It may also place its jaws over the other wolf's muzzle. The lower-ranked wolf crouches, tucks its tail between its legs, holds its ears flat and looks away from or up at the dominant wolf. It may also partially arch its back. If a high-ranked wolf wants to express its dominance in a more aggressive manner to a group of lower-ranked ones, it growls and bares its teeth, with its ears pointed. The subordinate wolves whimper, or they may surround the high-ranked wolf and put their noses up against it.

SAYING HELLO A grey wolf gently bites the muzzle of another as a form of greeting. Muzzle-biting is also used by high-ranking members of the pack to assert dominance and impose discipline.

When a wolf smells a scent, it can tell whether the wolf that left it was from its own pack or a stranger, whether it was an adult or juvenile and whether it was a male or female.

The frequent expression of relative rank helps to maintain order and, to a large extent, prevents fights from breaking out. In the rare event that a lower-ranked wolf challenges a higher-ranked one, the dominant wolf will point its ears forward, towards the other wolf, or more aggressively may crouch over the other, baring its teeth and growling. At this, the lower-ranked wolf will normally signal that it knows its place, and that the challenge is over, by flattening its ears against its head.

Scent-marking

A wolf has an extremely keen sense of smell – about 100 times more acute than a human's – so scent also plays an important part in lupine communication. Wolf packs use scent to mark the boundaries of their territories and also the areas around their kills. They do so by spraying urine on raised objects, such as trees, rocks and bushes, and by scratching the ground – this leaves a chemical trace because it stimulates scent glands located between the wolves' toes. The boundary scents warn other wolf packs to keep out. When a wolf smells a scent, it can tell whether the wolf that left it was from its own pack or a stranger, whether it was an adult or juvenile and whether it was a male or female. Within a pack, wolves can identify each other by their individual scents – so scent marks may also help a wolf find its way home, or to help others find it, should it become separated from the rest of the pack.

Vocalisation

Wolves make four main types of sound: howling, barking, growling and whimpering. They can use any of these sounds or a combination of them to communicate with other wolves. As with scent, every wolf is identifiable to the other members of its pack by its howl. So a lost wolf will sometimes howl alone to identify its location, until it finally becomes reunited with its pack. Wolves sometimes also howl alone to attract mates.

Wolf packs tend to howl both before and after going on a hunt. Before the hunt, group howling is used to excite the pack members and reinforce the bonds between them prior to setting out. When wolves return from a hunt, any pack members who stayed behind will often rush to greet the hunters, and howling will usually break out to celebrate if the hunt was successful. Group howls can also be used to warn off other wolf packs, which may hear

SCENT DETECTION A mother and her pups are working out the identity of the wolf that has recently left its scent on a tree in their territory.

the howls up to 15 km away. And sometimes wolf packs perform a group howl purely for social reasons, often accompanied by playful nuzzling and tail-wagging.

Wolves use barks, growls and whimpers mainly for short-distance communication. Barks are used as warning signals, most often when a wolf is surprised or attacked at its den, or to challenge another wolf – usually a stranger in a face-off. A growl is used to express anger and disapproval and to reinforce dominance. When a wolf growls, its hair will often rise and bristle. Adult wolves may growl to discipline pups or as a warning signal for them to return to the den. Growls are heard frequently when pups are learning how to hunt and fight by playing with each other. Whimpering portrays a friendly attitude. Pups may use it to ask for care, while adults may call pups out of the den in this manner. Also, pups (and sometimes adults) may whimper to express pain or fear. More commonly, adults whimper as a greeting or to show a submissive attitude when meeting a wolf of higher rank.

Tail talk

A wolf's tail is one of the most expressive parts of its anatomy. The tail of a wolf that senses danger, for example, points straight out, parallel to the ground. In contrast, a relaxed wolf's tail hangs down; the further down the tail droops, the more relaxed the wolf. A fearful wolf will tuck its tail between its legs, in the same manner as a wolf expressing lower rank. And just like a domesticated dog, a joyful or playful wolf will hold its tail up high and wag it. A wolf pup that bows down with its rear in the air, wagging its tail, is asking to play.

TALKING UNDERWATER

THE WORLD BENEATH THE SURFACE OF THE OCEANS IS BY NO MEANS A SILENT ONE. In fact, as they call and chat to each other, the animal inhabitants produce a near-deafening chorus of sound. On coral reefs, spiny lobsters make rasping noises to warn of danger by rubbing the lower parts of their antennae against a serrated ridge just below their eyes. On rocky or weed-covered bottoms, pistol shrimps make loud cracking sounds when attacking prey or defending their burrows. These little explosions are so loud that the shrimps compete with animals such as whales for the title 'loudest animal in the sea'. Male toadfish attract females with foghorn-like calls, releasing jets of air by contracting muscles in their swim bladders. Hogfish grind their teeth and sea-catfish make a noise like a tom-tom. At dawn and dusk, members of the wide-spread croaker family of fish make noises reminiscent of a pneumatic drill.

Visual communication is also widespread. Reef squid talk to each other through intricate changes in posture, colour and skin pattern. In caves, flashlight fish use bioluminescent torches below their eyes to communicate among themselves, to confuse predators and attract plankton.

By far the most accomplished communicators in the marine environment are the cetaceans, which include whales, dolphins and porpoises. Along with visual signalling, these mammals use an enormous variety of sounds to keep in touch with

DISTINCTIVE PATCHES Each orca has a unique black-and-white body pattern. This provides the easiest means of communicating its identity to other pod members over short distances.

other members of their own species, from trills and whistles at the higher frequency end of the sound spectrum, to grunts and groans at the lower end. They make sounds by pushing air past structures called phonic lips that project into the nasal passages below their blowholes. As air pushes through the nasal passages and past the phonic lips, the surrounding tissue vibrates, producing sound.

Orca talk

The large members of the dolphin family known as orcas, or killer whales, are expert communicators. There are at least three distinct types of orca, and they differ significantly in their patterns of communication. Resident orcas live in coastal waters, consistently visiting the same areas each year. They eat mainly fish and squid, and live in stable family groups, called pods, of about 8 to 15 individuals. Transient orcas feed on marine mammals, such as seals and porpoises, live in smaller, less cohesive pods of about two to six individuals, and roam more widely around coasts. Offshore orcas live in the open ocean, travelling in groups of up to 60 animals and feeding mainly on sharks, other fish and sea turtles.

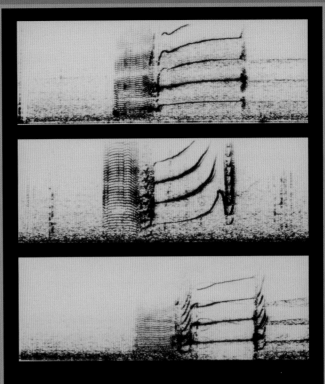

ORCA RECORDINGS
These sound spectographs show three different orca calls recorded over a time period of a few seconds. Each dark area on the graphs represents a sound lasting for a short period of time and containing either a mixture of frequencies or a single varying frequency. Orcas that use the same call are always in the same pod or closely related to each other, so visual sound recordings like these enable researchers to identify members of different pods.

All orcas produce three categories of sound, called clicks, whistles and burst-pulse sounds. The clicks are part of an orca's echolocation (sonar) apparatus, used for navigation and locating food sources. They are directed pulses of high-frequency sound that bounce off the objects they meet. The returning clicks are picked up by the orca that emitted them and interpreted to provide information about the objects' distance, shape and size.

Whistles are continuous emissions of shrill, frequency-modulated tones that last for a few seconds. Burst-pulse sounds, the main component of orca communication, are loud and complex combinations of sounds released in pulses with a high repetition rate (greater than about 300 pulses per second). To the human ear, they resemble a mixture of chirps, trills, whines, grunts, squeaks, burps, buzzes and the sound of creaking doors. Whistles and burst-pulse sounds are sometimes referred to as calls, as their assumed use is for communication rather than navigation or prey location.

Resident orcas are normally extremely vocal, producing frequent bursts of clicking and many calls while foraging. Each resident orca pod has its own collection of about a dozen discrete calls, although sometimes several related pods, forming larger acoustic groups called 'clans', share a few of their calls. The fact that the call repertoire of resident orca pods are specific to each pod means that the movements of different pods in particular ocean areas can be tracked by using hydrophones (underwater microphones). Listening in this way also gives clues to the purpose of the calls. Undoubtedly, one of their main functions is to provide positional information. The members of a pod are hardly ever out of hearing range of one another, so the calls let each member know where all the others are.

Transient orcas tend to be relatively quiet while travelling and foraging so as not to alert their prey, but become quite noisy when they do attack. Unlike resident orcas, transients do not display highly group-specific collections of calls: instead they all seem to use the same repertoire of about four to six distinct call types. The reason for this is that transients tend to have a more fluid social structure than residents – their pods split up and merge with other groups more frequently. Relatively little is known about the vocal patterns of offshore orcas, although it is known that their calls are completely different from those produced by resident or transient orca pods.

SPINNING LEAP A Hawaiian spinner dolphin jumps acrobatically out of the water and spins as fast as it can.

Body talk

Body posturing is an additional way in which dolphins exchange information. Body contact itself is used frequently to communicate fellowship. Dolphins are tactile animals and can often be observed caressing each other with their pectoral fins and flukes. Much of this physical contact is likely to reaffirm friendly relationships among individuals and groups. Aggression is often communicated by jaw clapping, the use of exaggerated movements, and swimming belly-up. Aggressive posturing can be a prelude to butting or even biting.

Spinner dolphins, which are found extensively in tropical and subtropical seas, perform spectacular acrobatic leaps out of the water, making as many as seven mid-air spins before landing back with a loud splash. The reason for this manoeuvre is not known. One suggestion is that the bubble vortex created by the dolphin's exit from the water – which is detectable by echolocation – signals its position to other pod members. Alternatively, the spinning may be a courtship display, a signal that the dolphin is ready to go hunting, or have some physical purpose such as to eject water from the dolphin's respiratory tract. Other actions frequently performed by spinner dolphins include head slaps (slapping the head on the surface of the water), thought to indicate a preferred direction to take, and tail slaps, which are thought to send messages about danger or may be a signal to dive.

BOTTLENOSE DOLPHINS POSSESS

ONE OF THE HIGHEST RATIOS OF BRAIN SIZE TO BODY MASS IN THE ANIMAL WORLD. The level and nature of their intelligence is still being researched, but it is clear that they are self-aware (they can recognise themselves in a mirror), can make and execute plans, are sociable and have a capacity for mimicry. They send accoustic messages to each other through a highly sophisticated communication system.

Altogether, bottlenose dolphins can make about 30 different types of whistles and burst-pulse sounds. Each dolphin has a unique signature whistle, which identifies it to other dolphins in its pod. They also use body language to communicate aspects of their emotional state and to convey a range of specific messages to close family members. Examples include jaw clapping, blowing bubbles, or slapping their tails or fins on the surface of the water when they are agitated or upset. A mother may express disapproval to her young by moving her head up and down. Bottlenoses frequently engage in synchronous movements to show their solidarity. Small groups may surface and swim together, turn simultaneously and even jump in unison. This type of behaviour is especially common during courtship displays.

VITAL STATISTICS

CLASS: Mammalia
ORDER: Cetacea
SPECIES: *Tursiops truncatus*
HABITAT: Coasts and upper waters of the open ocean
DISTRIBUTION: Worldwide, except for polar regions
KEY FEATURE: A highly sophisticated echolocation apparatus

NATURE'S POWERS

LONG-DISTANCE TALK

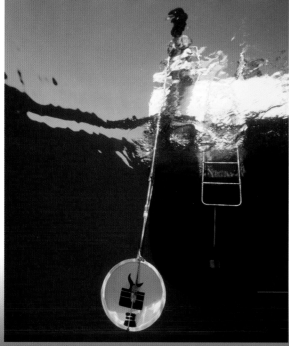

THE HAUNTING SONGS OF MALE HUMPBACK WHALES have been described as the most complex in the animal kingdom. They can be heard up to 160 km away and consist of low-pitched sounds, many of them repeated several times, varying in frequency and loudness. A song can last for up to 30 minutes, sometimes repeated over and over for several hours. Some humpbacks have been recorded singing for more than 24 hours at a time. What is perhaps most remarkable is that all the whales within a specific area, for example all the male humpbacks in the north Pacific, sing nearly the same song, with only slight variations, whereas whales in a different area, such as the south Atlantic, have a different song. Each song slowly evolves over time.

The exact purpose of whale song is not known, but because the songs are heard only during the mating season, the males probably use them to attract female whales. Whether they are a 'flirting' behaviour, a competitive behaviour between males trying to attract the same female, or a warning signal to other males to keep away from his territory (and the females it contains), is the subject of ongoing research.

Other whale talk

Fin and blue whales, and a number of other large whales, live in loose herds that are spread across large areas of ocean. Members of these herds communicate

LISTENING IN A hydrophone (left) records the long-distance calls of cetaceans, such as sperm whales and humpbacks (below).

BIG VOICE The siamang, a gibbon native to the forests of South-east Asia, has an inflatable throat pouch that allows it to make loud, resonating calls.

CARRYING CALL The Sulawesi red-knobbed hornbill emits a loud, barking call that can be heard for a distance of more than 2 km.

with loud sounds at frequencies of 10–40 Hz (the lowest frequency sound that a human can typically hear has a frequency of about 20 Hz). In blue whales these calls last for 10 to 30 seconds, in fin whales between one and two seconds, with various sound combinations in patterned sequences lasting up to 15 minutes. Blue whales in the Indian Ocean have been recorded producing songs lasting for a few minutes and consisting of four notes. The source of these sounds perplexed sailors for centuries.

Southern right whales choose the exact, fairly low frequency that carries their calls the greatest distance underwater, except on breeding sites where they intersperse these low-pitched grunts and moans with high-pitched squeals. Male North Atlantic right whales produce gunshot-like sounds that might function as a warning to other males to stay away. Sperm whales, unlike their baleen cousins, use high-pitched calls like dolphins. They congregate in family groups, and each whale has its unique, identifying combination of clicks.

Terrestrial communicators

Sound does not travel as far on land as in water, but there are a number of mammals and birds that communicate over long distances. Elephants send messages using low-frequency bellowing calls that travel up to 10 km, and vibrations transmitted through the ground that may also travel for several kilometres (see page 33). The siamang, the largest of all gibbons, lives in family groups of an adult male and female and, on average, two offspring. Their calls, often made by the family group in chorus, are thought to be directed towards siamang in neighbouring territories, which may be several kilometres away, warning them off their feeding territory. Male howler monkeys have the loudest calls of any land animal – a barking whoop or roar (rather than a howl) that can be heard clearly for distances of up to 5 km. The calls are thought to communicate information about the location and composition of the group to other howler monkey groups.

One component of the wood grouse or capercaillie's call is so low that humans cannot hear it. This low frequency, or infrasonic, sound can travel for several kilometres. Other birds with calls that travel particularly long distances include the kakapo of New Zealand and many species of hornbill. Southern ground hornbills communicate with loud, four-note booming calls that on a still day can be heard up to 5 km away. Great hornbills have a loud, distinctive call that is typically voiced at the onset of the breeding season or when the birds return to their roost. These vocalisations are used in defence of territory and for maintaining contact between members of the species.

SHOALS, SCHOOLS AND FLOCKS

CORAL CLUBS Large and spectacular shoals of glassfish (above) are common in and around caves close to Red Sea coral reefs. Keeping in tight formation, a school of giant parrotfish (below) swims through the waters of the Great Barrier Reef in Australia.

FISH AND BIRDS ARE SPECIALISTS AT PERFORMING LARGE-SCALE, SYNCHRONISED MOVEMENTS involving hundreds or even thousands of individuals. Fish – usually of the same species and sometimes in huge numbers – come together to form a social grouping known as a shoal. In most shoals, the fish still move fairly independently, but each one is attracted to other members of the group and adjusts its swimming action accordingly, so that the whole mass of animals remains coherent.

A school is a special type of shoal in which the fish synchronise their swimming in a highly regimented way – they move at exactly the same speed and in the same direction, maintain a set distance between their neighbours in a closely knit swimming pattern, and respond instantly to changes in the direction and speed of the other members of the school. Classic examples of shoaling and schooling fish include anchovies, sardines, herrings, sweepers, barracuda and grunts. A number of other marine animals also form similar groupings – in particular, krill (shoals) and dolphins (schools).

Shoaling helps to reduce the risk of predation, partly because many eyes help to detect predators and partly because of two other effects, known as dilution and confusion. The

CORAL CLUBS Large and spectacular shoals of glassfish (above) are common in and around caves close to Red Sea coral reefs. Keeping in tight formation, a school of giant parrotfish (below) swims through the waters of the Great Barrier Reef in Australia.

dilution effect relies simply on safety in numbers. In any given predator attack, a smaller percentage of a large shoal will be eaten compared to a small shoal (those on the outside edges are more likely to be caught than those in the centre). The confusion effect is based on the fact that shoaling fish are generally all silvery and a similar size, making it difficult for a predator to pick out an individual. A large shoal may even convince a predator that it has come across one enormous and formidable fish, rather than a mass of smaller ones.

Shoaling also provides increased efficiency in finding and snapping up food because of the presence of many eyes. Also, in schools the geometrical arrangement of the fish is a type of filter for trapping mobile prey. Shoaling can lead to increased reproductive success, because less energy has to be expended to find a mate within a shoal. Another advantage of schooling, in particular, is that it produces increased hydrodynamic efficiency. Because the fish in a school swim in a precise pattern, and the motions of their tails produce tiny vortices (swirling currents similar to little whirlpools), each fish can, in theory, use the vortices produced by the fish in front of it to reduce the friction on its own body. This allows all but the lead fish in a school to conserve energy when swimming, and may explain why the leadership of a school often changes.

Most schools (but not shoals) disperse after dark, suggesting that vision plays an important part in the schooling behaviour of species. With eyes located on the sides of the head, fish cannot focus directly forwards, but they are especially sensitive to lateral movement – an essential attribute in schooling. The fish can see what other members of the school are doing in relation to themselves and so can respond in an instant.

Laboratory experiments carried out on temporarily blinded fish support the hypothesis that sight is of prime importance in schooling, but in some species it was found that there was also another sense that played a key role. The lateral-line system is based on a string of pressure and movement-sensitive sensory cells that run in lines along the sides of many schooling fish. These lateral lines seem to be especially important to fish living in the murky waters of estuaries, where sight is not much use. It is also

possible that chemical pheromones play some role in schooling and shoaling behaviour, although so far no firm evidence for this has been found.

Balling behaviour

When some shoals of fish are startled or approached by predators, they will close into a compressed swirling sphere or 'ball'. Examples of balling species include sand lance and Pacific herring. One theory for how and why a fish ball forms is that

KRILL BALL Krill compact themselves into a tight mass as a defence against predators – in this case mackerel.

STAYING CLOSE Dunlin form particularly tight, compact flocks that can often be seen swirling in synchronised flight near their habitat on coastal mudflats or sandy beaches, as here at Jones Beach, New York.

each individual member of the group acts to reduce the danger to itself by swimming as close as possible to the centre of the group. So although the mass of fish might appear to act as a single unit, the spherical formation they create results from the uncoordinated behaviour of each self-protecting individual.

Bird flocks

Birds form flocks for many of the same reasons that fish shoal – for safety in numbers and to confuse predators, for energy conservation in the case of formation flying, and for accurate location of food and roosting sites. What is even more impressive in birds is how the large numbers in a flock can coordinate their formation flying in such a precise way. When observing flocks of dunlins, knots or starlings, for example, sudden changes in direction sometimes seem to occur instantaneously throughout the flock as though a sixth sense existed between the flock members. There are evidently no leaders in these bird flocks, at least not for more than a few seconds at a time – there cannot be, as different birds find themselves at the front of the flock every time it changes direction.

Analysis of slowed-down, high-speed film of species such as sandpipers has revealed what actually happens in these flying displays. It seems that to help avoid predation, it is advantageous for bird flocks to regularly make sudden and erratic changes of direction, and these movements are triggered by small, random fluctuations in the direction in which individual birds are flying. Every few seconds, one of these random fluctuations is big enough to trigger a reaction, within just a few hundredths of a second, in neighbouring birds. The reaction propagates through the flock in a wave radiating outwards from the initiation site and travelling close to the speed of light. Although the waves can move in any direction through the flock, including from back to front, a flock usually only responds to movements of birds that turn inwards, towards the centre of the flock. Birds turning away from the centre of the flock – particularly those already near its edge – run the risk of being separated from the rest of the flock and then picked off by a predator, so these types of movements are ignored.

When flocks are not under attack from a predator, but just beginning a flight from a roosting site to a feeding area, or vice-versa, initially they also dart to and fro in an apparently random fashion, as small movements by individual birds trigger off changes in direction. Eventually, a consensus emerges based on the motivation of the majority of the flock, and it flies off towards its destination in a more direct fashion.

STARLINGS

ONE OF THE GREATEST
GROUP-FLYING DISPLAYS IN NATURE OCCURS WHEN SEVERAL THOUSAND COMMON OR EUROPEAN STARLINGS COME TOGETHER IN A PULSATING MASS BEFORE THEY ROOST. In Denmark, where these displays are particularly impressive, the complex silhouettes that the starlings make against the sky on winter evenings are known as 'black sun'. The birds group into tight, often vaguely elliptical formations that expand, contract and constantly change shape without any apparent single leader. The aerial displays can last for 20 minutes or more, before small funnels of birds begin to drop out of the wheeling clouds to their roosting sites. Eventually, the whole group settles.

In common with some other avian flocking displays, there are many sudden synchronised changes in direction. These are undoubtedly an anti-predator device and are thought to be triggered off by small, random changes in direction by individual birds in the flock. Unlike most other flocks the starling formations quite frequently split but then quickly reform, as though drawn together by a magnetic force, or a gigantic invisible elastic band. The rapid reforming of a flock may be caused by individual birds making decisions on where to fly to next. The birds roost in extremely high densities to provide extra warmth on cold nights, and this probably accounts for the prolonged duration of the displays. As the birds congregate aerially, it can take a little time for the different groups of starling to identify their own roosting sites on the ground.

VITAL STATISTICS

CLASS: Aves
ORDER: Passeriformes
SPECIES: *Sturnus vulgaris*
HABITAT: Open woodland, cultivated land and urban areas
DISTRIBUTION: Europe, North America, Africa, western Asia and Australasia
KEY FEATURE: Flocking displays

BODY LANGUAGE

A DOMINANT MALE HIPPOPOTAMUS OPENS ITS HUGE MOUTH AS WIDE AS POSSIBLE, pushing its upper jaw almost vertically into the air to fully display its large teeth, tongue and the rest of the inside of its mouth. With this yawning display, which may be accompanied by other signals, such as head-shaking, grunting or roaring, the hippo is sending a clear message to any male that strays into its territory to keep away. Sometimes an intruder will respond with a yawn of its own, and if neither party backs off, the confrontation may lead on to a jaw-to-jaw pushing match, or more rarely an overt fight involving violent biting. Female hippos may perform milder forms of the same display when defending themselves or their offspring against male aggression.

As well as threat displays, body language can be used to communicate submission or acquiescence, to express an emotional state, such as fear or contentment, to strengthen pair bonds, or to attract or maintain the attention of potential mates. Gazelles, for example, assume characteristic poses as a signal to initiate mating. The male lowers and stretches his head and neck. The female responds

OPEN WIDE A face-off between two male hippos in Kenya's Masai Mara. The open mouths indicate a struggle for dominant status, and may be a prelude to a fight.

In any hierarchy, those with higher status tend to be accorded preferential access to resources, such as space, food and mating opportunities.

AROUND 30 DIFFERENT TYPES of hand gestures have been identified in the communication behaviour of chimpanzees and bonobos. These range from open-handed begging to a patting gesture used by dominant individuals when providing reassurance to a subordinate.

MORE THAN 25 DIFFERENT COMPONENTS HAVE BEEN IDENTIFIED IN SHARK THREAT DISPLAYS.

DEPENDING ON THEIR POSITION, HORSES' EARS CAN INDICATE ANGER, ALERTNESS, INTEREST, FEAR OR CONCENTRATION.

than the dominant individual's peers. In blue-clawed prawn society, male prawns with the bluest claws, which usually also happen to be the largest claws, dominate over larger rivals who have more pallid claws. Sometimes the ranking in a dominance hierarchy is determined partly on a hereditary basis. Thus, in some primates, including chimpanzees and olive baboons, dominance ranking among females is passed on from mothers to daughters.

In some birds, such as flocks of free-range chickens, the dominance hierarchy is literally a pecking order. The most dominant birds peck all the other birds and have first choice over resources, such as food. Those of lower rank can peck at some birds but are pecked by others of higher status. Those at the bottom of the hierarchy are pecked by all the other birds and have the least access to resources.

by walking away and circling round. She may then hold her tail out to signal that she is ready to submit to the male's advances.

Dominance hierarchies

An important concept related to the use of body language in animal communication is that of dominance hierarchies, also known as 'pecking orders'. In wolf packs, individual animals use body language to affirm their relative rank within a hierarchy whenever they meet (see page 116), and similar systems exist in many other animal groups. Sometimes separate dominance hierarchies exist in the males and females of a group, or there may be one hierarchy for the group.

In any hierarchy, those with higher status tend to be accorded preferential access to resources, such as space, food and mating opportunities. As a result, those animals with higher status tend to be more reproductively successful. The lower-ranked members acquiesce in the system on the basis that the dominant parties tacitly agree not to injure them, and may even protect them, provided they do not interfere with the dominant animals' access to resources. In evolutionary terms, pecking orders probably developed because they helped to reduce conflict within animal groups and thus the chances of injury among group members who share genes.

Dominance can be acquired and expressed in social animals through a number of mechanisms – by physical size, by tests of strength, or sometimes by the possession of a particular physical trait to a greater extent

Shark speak

Sharks use body language to express dominance hierarchies and to repel intruders. A great white shark will ram an intruding smaller shark in the gills if it does not back away. Sharks also use body posture to show relaxation or stress. Relaxed sharks swim with their bodies in a straight line, propelling themselves with their tails, and with their pectoral fins (the lower, front fins) pointing at an angle about 20° below the horizontal.

SQUABBLING VULTURES A combination of threat displays and aggressive pecking helps to establish who has precedence at a newly discovered carcass.

THREAT DISPLAY This type of blatant intimidatory fang-baring by an olive baboon is often used to quell mutinous behaviour among subordinates.

If a shark feels endangered, it typically produces a threat display to warn that it may attack if disturbed any further. The most common feature of a threat display, seen in all shark species, is a downward pointing of the pectoral fins, to an angle of about 60° below the horizontal. Another component of shark threat display is a hunched back – in grey reef sharks the posture can be held for up to 30 seconds – accompanied by an upward pointing snout. Other warning signs of potential aggression include exaggerated side-to-side body movements, with the shark almost folding itself in half, body shivers (seen only in silvertip sharks), jaw gaping, flank displays (turning sideways to the target and swimming slowly), and what is termed 'give way' behaviour – swimming straight at a target but turning away at the last moment.

PECKING ORDER At a bird table, the smaller blue tits yield to a great tit, which in turn will yield to a nuthatch.

Non-human primates

Much body language in non-human primates – the apes, monkeys and lemurs – is used to communicate needs, such as for food or affection, and to express emotions. Bonobos make a pouting face, in which the eyes are opened and the lips pushed forwards in an 'O' shape, in times of frustration or anxiety, such as after an attack or when an infant is lost. Pursing of the lips can mean a request for food, while the 'play face', where both eyes and mouth are open but the teeth are not showing, indicates enjoyment during play.

Primate body language may equally be concerned with the communication and maintenance of social status. The stretching out of a hand from one chimpanzee to another, for example, is an obvious appeal for sharing, but it may also reflect and reinforce the chimp's lower position in the dominance hierarchy.

Most primates, including humans, use threatening gestures, stares and poses to intimidate others. Body language employed in this way is termed agonistic and is usually sufficient to prevent physical fighting. In fact, physically violent encounters are rare among non-human primates. The dominant male in a community of apes or baboons can usually prevent major conflicts and keep order by the use of often subtle agonistic displays. One tactic of male baboons is to flash their eyelids. If this does not do the trick, they open their mouths into a wide yawn.

FRIENDLY GESTURES Lions constantly express their affection by nuzzling and licking one another's faces. Communicating in this way reinforces bonds and helps to keep a pride together.

Primates also use a range of submissive body language, which in olive baboons includes crouching down in a rigid position, grinning and erecting the tail. Most primate species communicate affection and reduce group tension by sitting close to each other, touching and mutually grooming. Mutual grooming, in particular, is used by both monkeys and apes to reinforce male–female pair bonds as well as same-sex friendship bonds. Chimpanzees often engage in bouts of mutual grooming that can go on for hours – typically, a dominant chimp will demand to be groomed by sitting with its back to a subordinate. Chimps also groom each other to calm their emotions following aggressive outbursts by angry dominant males.

The organisation of dominance hierarchies in primates varies considerably between species. Olive baboons have fairly stable, separate hierarchies among both males and females, while hamadryas baboons live in a highly male-dominated society, the alpha males effectively suppressing the development of any hierarchy among the females, which are of uniformly low rank. In contrast, in groups of mantled howler monkeys in South and Central America, young reproductively active females have a relatively high rank within their groups.

Bird displays

When a bird clicks its beak, it is communicating that it feels threatened. A bird approaching another bird with its head down and face feathers puffed out is asking to be preened, whereas one that is crouched down with its beak open and flaring its tail feathers may be giving a warning to another bird or other intruder to back off. Unlike humans, birds are able to control their irises, enlarging and shrinking their pupils rapidly. A bird 'flashing' its pupils in this way may be excited, frightened or aggressive.

Birds in lasting pair bonds often engage in symmetrical displays with each other. Notable examples include the ritual mating displays of great crested grebes, which include complex head shaking and bobbing, and the triumph displays performed by many species of geese, in which they wave their necks and honk loudly at one another after victorious confrontations with other geese.

Feline affections

Wild and domestic cats communicate their emotional state to each other with body language that can involve their ears, eyes, tails and overall body posture. Particular combinations of posture can reveal whether the animal is in relaxed, fearful, aggressive, tolerant or defensive mood. Triggered by fear, a rush of adrenaline will cause a cat's back and tail to arch and its hair to bristle. When cats are fearful and defensive, their ears flatten and their eyes widen to take in as much of their surroundings as possible. The body language of confident, aggressive cats can be seen in confrontations with other cats that intrude into their territories. Their pupils narrow for better depth perception as they stare down opponents, and their ears prick up, facing forwards.

Big cats such as lions also use body language to communicate the way they feel. A lion flicking its tail with its head held low may be threatening attack. Any lion that shows its teeth is likely to be angry or fearful, although a young lion whose mouth is open without showing its teeth is indicating that it is ready to play. When members of a pride meet, they greet each other in a ritualised way to strengthen their bonds. First they sniff each other's noses, then they rub heads and sides, and may drape their tails across each other's backs.

PLANT
GROUPS

BRACKEN PROLIFERATES ON A SCOTTISH MOORLAND TO THE EXCLUSION OF ALMOST EVERYTHING ELSE. Some plants, like bracken, have a chemical armoury that inhibits competitors from gaining a foothold. Not all plants adopt such aggressive colonising techniques, but it is by forming communities that they are best able to ensure the survival of the species. For pollination to occur, most plants must enlist the services of pollinators such as insects. It is a precarious business, full of possible pitfalls, and by grouping together, synchronising blossoming times and producing lots of pollen, the plants have the best chance of success. The same strategy of strength in numbers applies to seed production. The more seeds there are, the greater the chances of one landing in the right place, making it through to germination and becoming the next generation of the plant.

There are some plants that follow the phases of the Moon. The night-flowering Queen of the Night cacti of Central and South America bloom close to a full moon.

LOADING UP A lily flower's anthers are laden with pollen grains, which stick to visiting insects, such as this cricket. Fertilisation occurs when pollen is successfully transferred by the pollinator to the female parts of the flower.

A TIME TO FLOWER

EACH SPRING IN JAPAN, AS A WARM FRONT MOVES UP FROM THE SOUTH, ornamental cherry trees burst into a profusion of blossom, which lasts for just a few days before the delicate petals fall. Although ethereally beautiful, coordinated displays such as this serve a serious purpose: reproduction. Plants of the same type bloom together so that they can cross-pollinate and ensure a good mix of genes, giving their offspring the best chance of survival.

When pollen from one flower reaches the heart of a flower on a different plant of the same species, fertilisation takes place and the plant sets seed. The fact that pollen travels between plants is important as it ensures a good mixing of genes in the subsequent generation, but it is a precarious journey that relies on two things: a courier of some kind and good timing.

Many of the showiest flowers are pollinated by insects or birds, which inadvertently pick up pollen grains while visiting the flowers to drink the sugary nectar. They then carry the pollen to the next flower they visit. But even with this 'door-to-door' service, most of the pollen grains are lost in transit, land on the wrong flower, or are even consumed by insects, so plants make copious amounts.

Flowers that use the wind as a courier service, such as grasses and some trees, produce the largest amounts of pollen. They have to, because wind is indiscriminate in the direction it blows; with enough pollen carried on the breeze, at least some of it is likely to reach its target. Just one birch-tree catkin may release up to five and a half million pollen grains into the air, which when multiplied by the thousands of catkins on a mature tree soon leads to high pollen concentrations in the air.

It does not matter how much pollen a flower produces if no other flowers are open to receive it, so – like Japan's ornamental cherry trees – plants synchronise their blossoming times. There are various environmental cues that help them to coordinate. In temperate zones the changing daylength and rising soil temperature are important triggers – in spring, for example, bulbs that have lain dormant burst into flower in unison, carpeting woodland floors. In the tropics, plants respond to the changing patterns of rainfall that denote 'rainy' and dry seasons.

There are some plants that follow the phases of the Moon. The night-flowering Queen of the Night cacti of Central and South America bloom close to a full moon. Each of the enormous fragrant flowers opens for just one night, so it is vital that plants synchronise their efforts. In deserts, such as south-western Africa's Namaqualand, seasonal rainfall is the signal that plants wait for. The parched African soil turns into a rainbow of colours, as plants quickly sprout up and flower.

CHERRY BLOSSOM Japanese cherry trees, known as sakura, blossom in unison in spring, with each tree in glorious full bloom for just a few days. For the Japanese, the cherry blossom season is a time of celebration. Japan's Meteorological Agency keeps a watchful eye on a cherry tree at the Yasukuni Shrine in Tokyo. When more than 80 per cent of the tree has come into bloom, they declare the hanami *(looking at flowers) season open.*

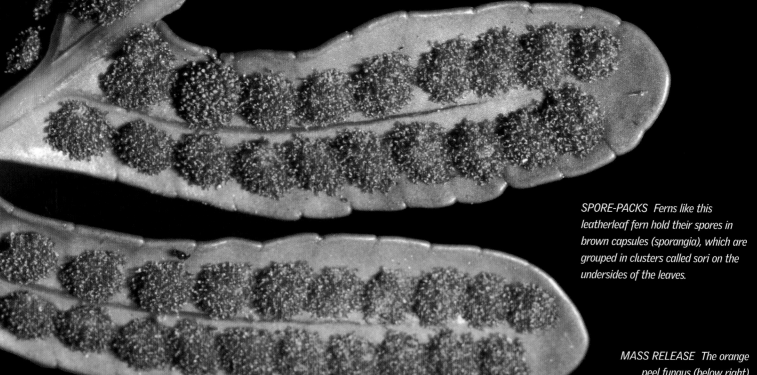

SEEDS AND SPORES

IT IS BY PRODUCING SEED THAT PLANTS ENSURE THE SURVIVAL OF THEIR SPECIES, but germination is never guaranteed. By the age of around 70 or 80, a mighty oak will produce thousands of acorns each year, but only a tiny fraction of these will ever grow into mature trees. Stuck with whatever position they land in, and unable to move, the acorns' fate is sealed. Those that do not travel far from the parent tree may be doomed as they remain in its shadow, while others are taken as food by woodland animals, such as squirrels – although those collected by jays and buried beneath a hedgerow stand a much better chance. Those acorns that do make it through to the sapling stage face competition for nutrients and sunlight from other plants, or may be nibbled off by deer.

Given these bleak odds, it is hardly surprising that plants produce seeds in enormous quantities and have developed ingenious dispersal strategies to ensure that the seed travels as far as possible. Some literally catapult the seed into the air as their seedpods dry out; others, such as poppies, have 'salt shaker' seed capsules that disperse the tiny seeds on the wind. Dandelions are among those plants whose seeds bear fluffy 'parachutes' so that they can be carried far and wide on the slightest breeze. Sometimes plant seeds hitch a ride on the fur of animals, their prickly hooks easily catching hold as an animal brushes past. Many plants encase their seeds in a sweet fleshy covering to tempt animals into eating it. The seed may travel through the gut of the animal and so be carried far away from the plant. When it passes out of the animal's gut it is accompanied by manure – a perfect germination medium.

Most seeds carry a supply of food to enable them to wait until the best moment to germinate. Some can survive several years in the open and there have been cases where seeds known to be hundreds of years old have germinated. Orchid seeds do not have that luxury. Unlike other seeds, they carry no food reserves whatsoever. Instead they rely on meeting up with a special kind of fungus that lives in the soil. Any seeds that do not meet the matched fungus soon perish, but those that do strike up a unique relationship, with the fungus supplying the germinating seed with all the energy and nutrients it requires. Most orchids produce thousands of minute seeds, some as many as five million

SWEET TEMPTATION If left to ripen on the bush, pomegranates burst open to advertise their jewel-like seeds, which are coated in a sweet-tasting flesh. Birds swallow the seeds whole and so help to distribute them.

from a single ovary. With so many seeds floating like dust on the air, there is a chance that at least a few will land close to the right fungal partner.

The success of spores

Before seed plants evolved, the Earth was colonised by spore-bearers, some of which, including ferns, mosses and liverworts, thrive to this day. Ferns produce clusters of spore capsules, called sori, in little brown patches on the undersides of their leaves. As the capsules mature they split open, releasing the minute spores. The numbers released are vast – 300 million from one bracken leaf alone – and although some fall to the earth quickly, others may be swept up by the wind and transported hundreds of miles.

Unlike seeds, spores do not contain embryo plants. When a fern spore lands in a suitable patch of moist ground, it grows into a tiny heart-shaped plant just 0.5 cm tall that looks nothing like a fern. The tiny green plants grow special male and female sex cells (both on the same plant), and the male cells have to swim, rather like sperm, to meet up with the female cells. After fertilisation, a new plant emerges that develops into a fully fledged fern, with a spreading root system and numerous sets of leaves (or fronds). It seems a precarious life cycle, yet ferns are found on every continent except Antarctica.

Fungi are another highly successful group of spore-bearers. Hidden below ground they form a mass of tangled threads collectively called a mycelium. The mushrooms or toadstools that appear above ground are the fruiting bodies and their purpose is to release spores – millions of them. It has been estimated that a single mushroom may release ten thousand million spores. Some fungi simply shake their spores out, while others squeeze them out. Some, such as the puffball fungus, have developed a way to project the spores explosively through the air.

CLONE POWER

PLANTS HAVE THE REMARKABLE ABILITY TO TURN A SMALL PIECE OF THEMSELVES INTO A NEW PLANT. The plant that grows will be genetically identical to the parent plant and known as a clone. Horticulturists harness this ability to propagate thousands of new plants from a desirable specimen. Some plants in the wild have also perfected this strategy – known as vegetative reproduction – creating huge numbers of the original plant. Some, such as the chandelier plant, produce tiny plantlets at the tips of their leaves, which drop to the soil and take root; others send out long, creeping stems that eventually send up a new plant some distance from the parent. Though vegetative reproduction does not have the advantage of mixing the genes, as occurs in sexual reproduction, it enables the plant to expand quickly, maximising its chances of outcompeting other species.

INVASION FORCE Prolific seed production – 100 000 from one plant – and aggressively spreading roots that send up clones combine to make rosebay willowherb a formidable weed.

One of the most prodigious space invaders is rosebay willowherb, which reproduces both sexually and vegetatively. This perennial plant of waste ground and open woodland spreads by creeping rhizomes (fleshy underground stems) that travel laterally by about 1 m per year, periodically sending up new plants. The plant quickly forms huge, dense clumps, where nothing else can get a foothold. Also known as fireweed because it is one of the first plants to grow back after a fire, rosebay willowherb produces huge numbers of seeds – up to 500 per seedpod – attached to fluffy parachutes that carry them far and wide.

plants are clones, and so genetically the same, it has been claimed that Japanese knotweed is the biggest female on earth.

Old clones

The steady production of clones means that some plants are virtually immortal. Since all the clones have the same genetic make-up as the parent, it can be argued that they are the same plant. The trembling aspens of North America are a good example. Each stand of trees is actually one organism that sends up trees from a network of roots. The individual trees may live 200 years or so, but the roots may be thousands of years old. Even if the trees are destroyed by wild fire, the root network, safe below ground, simply sends up new trees, making the most of the nutrient-rich ash that covers the ground after fire. Stands of trembling aspen are commonly 10 000 years old and the oldest – a 40-hectare patch in Utah known as Pando, or the trembling giant – is thought to be 80 000 years old.

Japanese knotweed was originally from eastern Asia but is now a pernicious weed throughout Europe, North America, Australia and New Zealand. The plant, which grows to 2 m in one season, does not set seed but spreads by an extensive rhizome system, which can be as thick as an arm and extend some 2 m below ground. The tall leafy stems soon overshadow neighbouring plants, while the rhizomes exude chemicals that inhibit the roots of other plants. The thick rhizomes store energy so that the shoots of Japanese knotweed are remarkably strong, capable of breaking through tarmac and can lie dormant in the soil for decades. An added concern for anyone trying to eradicate the weed is that a new plant can grow from just a pea-sized piece of rhizome or stem. So unless the utmost care is taken, clearing one infestation can easily lead to an outcrop of several new ones as tiny pieces of the plant are carried away on boots and the wheels of cars. Since all the

Another long-lived clone is the creosote bush that grows in the hot deserts of North America. The plant develops a characteristic circular growth pattern because it sprouts new clones from the tips of its roots. Eventually, the original plant dies, and the clones are left growing in a ring. They then sprout new clones from the tips of their roots, and so the diameter of the ring steadily increases. Growth is slow – around 1 m every 500 years – and measurements of the largest rings indicate some that can trace their clone origins back for 11 000 years.

SLOW BUT SURE Creosote bushes live long, slow lives. They colonise new land by sending up plants at the tips of their roots, creating a ring of new growth.

EXCLUDING OTHERS

IN ORDER TO DETER THE COMPETITION, MANY OF THE INVASIVE PLANTS THAT SPREAD VEGETATIVELY HAVE AN ARSENAL OF NASTY CHEMICALS AT THEIR DISPOSAL. In a kind of chemical warfare, the plants exude substances that make it difficult for neighbouring plants to take root. The process, known as allelopathy, can sometimes be harnessed by farmers to protect their crops by inhibiting weeds.

Inhibitory chemicals can be present in any part of the plant, including leaves, roots, fruit and stems or bark, and they target neighbouring plants in various ways. Some inhibit growth, preventing germination of seeds or deterring root and shoot growth; others affect the nutrient uptake so that in effect the rival plant starves. Plants that are known to be allelopathic

TOWERING THREAT The fast-growing tree of heaven has toxic chemicals in its roots that kill off other plants growing nearby. Tolerant of drought and pollution, the tree is known as the ghetto palm in New York.

include bracken, rhododendron, eucalyptus and tobacco.

A valuable hardwood tree, the black walnut (*Juglans nigra*) produces a chemical called juglone that is strongest in its roots, nut hulls and buds. The respiratory poison saturates the soil, especially at the drip line beneath the canopy, deterring plants from growing anywhere near, with the result that mature trees are often seen growing in areas of bare land. The toxin is particularly effective against members of the Solanaceae family (including tomatoes, peppers, deadly nightshade and potatoes), which soon wilt and die if planted beneath the tree's canopy.

Another plant with the reputation of a killer is *Ailanthus altissima*, commonly known as the tree of heaven because of its rapid growth, reaching around 20 m in 30 years. The tree is native to China, where its roots, leaves and bark are used in herbal medicine. It was first introduced to Britain in 1751 and thence to America, and it has been spreading ever since, a pattern that has accelerated in recent years with climate change. The tree produces seed in abundance and its invasive root system leaches toxins into the ground, preventing other plants in the vicinity from taking hold. Another weapon in its armoury is a rather unpleasant smell exuded by the male flowers, which is said to resemble rancid cashews. To add to the gardener's woes, the tree of heaven is notoriously difficult to eradicate. It responds to cutting by sending up lots of new shoots and, some distance from the original, it will send up new plants, or suckers, from its wide-ranging roots. These shoots quickly turn into tough new trees and eventually form a dense thicket which no other plants can penetrate. Like Japanese knotweed the shoots are vigorous and can damage pavements, literally cracking them open as it forces its way up.

Herbicidal action

There are cases where the noxious chemicals produced by plants can be harnessed as natural herbicides. Sorghum is a type of grass, originally from Africa, that is now grown widely throughout the tropics and subtropics as a staple grain to make flour, porridge and beer. In the USA it is grown mainly as animal feed, though its use as a grain by humans is gaining popularity. One advantage of sorghum is the plant's ability to

PUSH-PULL FARMING
In areas of eastern Africa, farmers have adopted a system of farming known as push-pull as a viable alternative to commercial pesticides. Push-pull involves intercropping a main crop with plants that repel pests ('push'), while plants grown around the perimeter attract (or 'pull') the pests. Here (right), a main crop of maize is intermixed with rows of low-growing silverleaf desmodium, which releases chemicals that repel the parasitic African witchweed (striga), which attacks maize roots. The desmodium also repels stemborer moths, whose grubs feed inside maize stems, while napier grass planted around the perimeter of the field pulls in the moths. An additional benefit of the system is that the companion plants provide valuable forage for farm animals.

deter weeds. A compound known as sorgoleone, which is present in sorghum's stems and roots, is highly effective at fighting weeds. Farmers make use of sorghum's weed-fighting nature by growing it as a cover crop between sowings of the main crop. The sorghum is cut down and the residue left on the soil or dug in, so that the chemicals within can leach into the soil, clearing weeds and giving the subsequent crop a fighting start.

VERSATILE GRAIN As well as being an important grain crop, sorghum has a toxic effect on weeds. It is often grown in rotation with other crops and dug into the soil to make use of its inhibitory effects.

ON THE ISLAND OF BORNEO, GREAT SWATHES OF BIODIVERSE RAIN FOREST HAVE BEEN **razed to make way for one single but lucrative crop – oil palms, the oil of which is in demand the world over.** Growing just one crop, usually on a large scale, to the exclusion of all others brings economic advantages. By cultivating just one particular variety of wheat, for example, a farmer can maximise land usage. Competition for resources from other plants is eliminated and as the crop is of a uniform height and ripens at the same time, harvesting is more efficient and can be easily mechanised. The farmer is also able to adjust the soil conditions more precisely to that particular crop.

Monocultures took off after World War II, when factories that had once made explosives began to churn out fertilisers instead. Dwarf varieties of wheat that did not fall over (or lodge) in the wind were crossbred with high-yielding varieties, and led to a dramatic improvement in yields. The same interbreeding of rice varieties also took place and there is little doubt that the 'green revolution', as it was called, prevented the starvation of millions of people. But there is a downside to this dependence on monocultures, not least, as in the case of Borneo, the devastation of existing ecosystems.

Since all the plants in a monoculture crop are genetically identical, if disease strikes, it blights the whole crop. As a precaution, farmers frequently apply pesticides, becoming locked in a vicious cycle as pests develop resistance and more pesticides are needed. Growing one single crop also places a much greater drain on the nutrients in the soil, so the farmer has to apply chemical fertilisers regularly.

The cost of cotton

Cotton is one of the most intensively grown crops on earth. There are several hundred types of insect that attack cotton, in particular the boll weevil, and consequently huge quantities of highly toxic insecticides are used in its production. Planted in large

CIDER APPLES Spring blossom covers the serried rows of apple trees in an orchard in Avon, England.

MONOCULTURES

COTTON HARVEST *Mechanised farming is indiscriminate, it takes everything, so a farmer must wait until most of the seedpods, or bolls, are ripe.*

monoculture fields, cotton requires a large input of fertilisers to achieve high yields. And before harvesting, the crop is drenched in yet another chemical – a defoliant that makes the harvesting of the bolls more efficient. This wholesale use of chemicals means that every year worldwide around 10 per cent of all agrochemicals and 25 per cent of all insecticides end up being applied to cotton crops.

Yet it is possible to grow crops and gain good yields without excessive use of agrochemicals. Most farmers now appreciate the problems associated with indiscriminate pesticide use and operate integrated pest management, where smaller, more precise applications of pesticides are combined with other practices, such as crop rotation, to improve soil fertility. In the case of cotton, there is a growing demand for organically produced fibre, where biological pest control replaces conventional pesticides, and nitrogen-fixing cover crops are used to fertilise the soil. Biological control involves many methods that are specific to the target pest and the region, including planting trap crops that lure the pests away from the cotton and strip cropping, whereby harvestable strips of two or more different crops are planted in the same field.

CASH CROP *Palm-oil plantations on Borneo are undermining the biodiversity of the island. One of the victims of the destruction of Borneo's rain forests is the orang-utan, which is now seriously endangered.*

BOOM
AND BUST

7

POPULATION BOOMS, OFTEN FOLLOWED OR PRECEDED BY DECLINES, ARE BY NO MEANS UNUSUAL IN THE NATURAL WORLD. Factors such as disease, human interference, unusual weather, stress from overcrowding, or the appearance of new competitor or predator species can cause sudden and catastrophic population falls. So can natural disasters, such as the eruption of the Alcedo volcano in the Galápagos Islands nearly 100 000 years ago that almost certainly accounted for a near wipe-out of the subspecies of giant tortoise that lives on the slopes of the volcano (left). Conversely, conditions that favour a species – such as a decline in a predator population, food becoming more plentiful, humans protecting rather than killing a species, or rains falling where previously there was a drought – can produce a sudden population boom.

PLAGUES

Rodent scourge

In the summer of 2007, an area of Spain's northern plain around
León and Valladolid was struck by a plague of over 700 million
common voles that devastated crops of lettuce, potato, beet and
barley and threatened to invade public parks, vineyards and even
city centres. There were so many that the smell of them filled the
air, and in some areas 80 per cent of crops were lost. Changes in
farming practices, together with a mild start to the year and a
fruitful spring, were thought to have triggered the sudden

*SEED-GLEANERS   A dense gathering of red-wing
blackbirds are alarmed while feeding on a field of corn
stubble. Flocks of several hundred red-wings are a
common sight across North America in late summer.*

population explosion. Eventually, the Spanish authorities resorted
to controlled burning of harvested fields (allowed by EU regulations
in exceptional circumstances) in an attempt to stamp out the
voles, although the outbreak was already subsiding as the voles'
food ran out, repeating similar cycles in 1988–9 and 1993–4.

Bird plagues

A few bird species congregate in sufficiently large numbers to be
considered a major scourge in some places. In sub-Saharan Africa,
flocks of red-billed quelea (a type of finch) are feared more than
locust swarms as they can cause serious and widespread crop
devastation. In parts of North America, red-winged blackbirds are
similarly unpopular because of their penchant for forming dense
congregations at the end of their breeding period. Sometimes
numbering millions, the flocks feed on corn, rice and sunflower
seeds. The birds also harbour a contagious fungal organism that
can cause a serious lung infection in humans.

TENT-DWELLERS A group of eastern tent caterpillars roam around their nest in a cherry tree. This species can completely defoliate their host tree.

Insect invasions

During the hot, dry summer of 1976, the UK and parts of Europe suffered a plague of ladybirds. Swarms became so large that car drivers had to use their wipers to clear the insects from their windscreens. Ladybirds were also biting people, a behaviour that had never previously been reported. The probable reason was that their usual food source, aphids, had run out and the ladybirds bit people in a desperate attempt to find something to eat. The ladybirds in this plague were native European species. More recently, the harlequin ladybird from Japan has spread across the USA and Canada, finally reaching the UK and mainland Europe. So far no swarms have developed as large as those seen in 1976.

In North America, the caterpillars of certain related species of moths are notorious for population booms and busts. The presence of the caterpillars in spring is usually signalled by their conspicuous nests, or 'tents', which they construct in the forks of trees. Every eight to ten years, large-scale outbreaks occur during which these pests become so abundant they are capable of defoliating tens of thousands of acres of forest and fruit trees.

INVADING LADYBIRDS Following their first appearance in the UK in 2004, harlequin ladybirds have already become the dominant ladybirds in south-east England. They eat other ladybird species as well as aphids.

ALIEN INVASIONS

POSSUM AND PUP About the size of a well-fed domestic cat, the brushtail possum from Australia now outnumbers humans in New Zealand by 17 to 1.

SOME SPECIES THAT ARE INTRODUCED INTO NEW LOCATIONS UNDERGO SPECTACULAR POPULATION BOOMS. This is particularly likely if the species has few or no competitors or predators in its new territory, but does have plenty of suitable food resources.

Successful invasions by alien species can be extremely damaging to the ecosystems into which they are introduced. These species can also have a negative effect on agriculture, and on the health of other animals and humans, and are recognised as a main cause of biodiversity loss second only to habitat destruction. Some have attained special notoriety, either for the sheer scale of the population increase or for the incongruence of the invaders in their new home.

A typical example of the harmful effect that a non-native species can have is the brushtail possum in New Zealand. European settlers introduced the possum, an Australian marsupial, into New Zealand in 1837 with the intention of establishing a fur industry. In Australia, the possums have a number of predators, including dingoes, owls and pythons, which keep their numbers in check. New Zealand has no such predators, but what it does have is just the sort of forest habitat that the brushtail possum loves. Their population has snowballed to about 70 million and they have become a major ecological threat. The main damage has been to New Zealand's forests, especially broad-leaved trees as the possums feed on the foliage and fruit. The possums also eat the eggs of New Zealand birds, and they are carriers of the organism that causes bovine tuberculosis in deer and cattle.

Home from home

Australia is itself the victim of ecological difficulties caused by non-native species, ranging from red foxes and rabbits to mynah birds, feral cats and giant mimosa trees. But possibly the most irksome invader over the past 50 years has been an amphibian – the impressively large and prolifically breeding cane toad.

Cane toads originate from tropical and subtropical America. They were introduced to Australia to control a species of beetle that was damaging sugarcane plantations in Queensland. The toads could not catch the beetles, which flew too high over their heads, but they proved well suited to their new environment. Since the original release of 40 toads in the 1930s, they have bred rapidly and now number more than 200 million. The toads have also expanded their range from Queensland into New South Wales and the Northern Territory. Some toads on the leading edge of this westerly advance have evolved larger legs, enabling them to travel faster. It is estimated that they can migrate at an average of 40 km per year.

Cane toads secrete a powerful toxin through their skin. In its native range, the toad has many predators that either tolerate this toxin or avoid the poisonous parts of the toad. In Australia the toxin kills most potential predators, whether they eat the toad or its tadpoles, and populations of marsupials, snakes and lizards have been decimated in areas where the toad has become established.

In the UK, one of the most noticeable recent population explosions has been that of the rose-ringed parakeet from the foothills of the Himalayas. What began in the 1960s as a tiny population, mainly in south-east England, is expected to reach over 50 000 or more by 2010. Nobody knows how the birds came to the UK; according to one theory, a small number escaped from a film studio in 1951 during the making of *The African Queen*. Naturalists fear that the parakeets are endangering native British birds, such as owls and woodpeckers, as they compete for nest sites. And they can decimate fruit-tree blossoms, causing heavy crop losses.

AVIAN IMMIGRANT Rose-ringed parakeets have gone native in the UK and thrive because they have no natural predators and suburban gardens provide a steady supply of seeds, nuts, berries and fruit.

INSATIABLE TOAD Cane toads not only consume food eaten by native Australian tree frogs, they also eat the frogs.

THERE IS MORE GENETIC VARIATION WITHIN SOME WEST AFRICAN CHIMPANZEE TROOPS than in the whole human population. Low levels of genetic diversity are also present in modern cheetahs, European bison and northern elephant seals.

If the population of a species declines severely and then recovers, the recovering population descends from the relatively small number of individuals who survived the population 'bust'. The genetic diversity in the recovering population is therefore less than in the original population. A decline and recovery episode severe enough to produce a significant reduction in a species' genetic diversity is known as a genetic or population bottleneck. The more severe the population decline – which in the worst case may reduce a species to just one breeding pair – the more pronounced is the lack of genetic diversity in the emergent population. The lack of diversity

GENETIC BOTTLENECKS

TOO-CLOSE FAMILY? A cheetah and her cubs look out from the top of a termite mound. The cheetah population is highly inbred, with hardly any variation in its DNA.

can reduce the ability of a species to adapt to future changes in its environment, or to fight off threats such as infectious diseases.

By examining the genes within a population, and particularly the amount of genetic variation between individuals, scientists have identified numerous bottlenecks. Additional genetic analysis can sometimes give clues to how long ago the bottlenecks occurred, and this information is also of interest to scientists seeking to date catastrophic events in Earth's past, as catastrophic events are a possible cause of severe population declines. The human population has probably been affected by a series of bottlenecks. During the most recent, about 70 000 years ago, the population is thought to have dwindled to fewer than 10 000 individuals living in East Africa. This coincided with a gigantic eruption of Toba, a volcano in northern Sumatra. Gas from the eruption formed a long-lasting haze that blocked out sunlight, and this may have caused a prolonged global cooling that triggered drought and famine in East Africa.

Cheetahs have extremely low levels of genetic variation due to a severe bottleneck that saw the population drop to as few as 10 individuals. The timing of the decline is not known for certain, but it

COMMON ANCESTORS Juvenile elephant seals bask on a California beach. They are part of a current population of more than 100 000, but all members are genetically very similar.

AMERICAN BISON The 350 000 or so bison that now roam parts of North America are descended from about 500 individuals that survived at the end of the 1880s.

may have been around the end of the last ice age, approximately 10 000 years ago, when the extinction of many large mammals occurred on several continents. Cheetahs survived probably only as a result of some brother-sister matings.

Among the Galápagos giant tortoises, the comparatively large population on the slopes of Alcedo volcano on Isla Isabela is genetically much less diverse than the other giant tortoise subspecies on the island. Genetic studies have indicated that a bottleneck occurred around 88 000 years ago – about the same time that the volcano erupted. It is probable that the two events are connected: the eruption would have buried much of the tortoise's habitat in layers of ash and lava, destroying most of its food sources.

For some species, the causes of a bottleneck are clear-cut. The northern elephant seal, which breeds on coasts and islands off California and western Mexico, was hunted to near extinction by humans in the 19th century. Recent calculations indicate that there may have been a single-year bottleneck around the end of the century of less than 20 seals. Because elephant seals breed harem-style, with a single bull mating with a group of females, just one male may have fathered all of the offspring during that bottleneck.

Both the European bison, or wisent, and the North American bison, or buffalo, have been through recent genetic bottlenecks. Today, a total of around 4000 European bison roam in the wild, and they are all descended from 17 animals that lived in zoos in the first half of the 20th century. Because of their limited gene pool, these populations are vulnerable to diseases such as foot and mouth.

An estimated 40–70 million bison roamed North America before 1800, but as a result of hunting by European settlers only about 500 remained by the 1880s. Fortunately, the reduction in genetic diversity caused by the bottleneck was not too severe as the surviving bison were located in several widely separated and genetically distinct herds.

ONE OF THE MOST FAMOUS BOOM-AND-BUST CYCLES IN THE NATURAL WORLD REVOLVES AROUND A SMALL ARCTIC MAMMAL – THE LEMMING. Various species of these hamster-like rodents inhabit parts of Canada, Alaska, Greenland, Scandinavia and Russia.

Lemmings do not hibernate in winter; they remain active, finding food by burrowing through the snow. People used to believe that when lemmings ran into a food shortage, they banded together and flung themselves off cliffs in a mass suicidal rush, but this tale has little basis in fact. The true story of the lemming population's booms and busts is, nevertheless, a fascinating and complex one.

Population cycles

Lemming populations sometimes explode spectacularly to 100 or even 1000 times their original size, then contract just as quickly, mainly in response to fluctuations in the populations of predators, which vary according to location. In Greenland, the main lemming predators are snowy owls, stoats, Arctic foxes and long-tailed skuas (a seabird); in other areas the short-eared owl and ermine feature strongly.

Booms in lemming numbers tend to occur when predator populations drop sharply. Favourable conditions, such as a short winter, can also help. As lemming numbers increase, predator numbers also grow until they become so numerous and eat so many lemmings that rodent numbers plummet. This is followed by a decline in the predator population. In Greenland, stoats are specialist predators that feed only on lemmings, so when lemming numbers fall, the stoat population begins to decline within a year. Other predators have alternative food supplies, so the population fall takes longer to become established. This sensitivity in different predator populations to fluctuations in the lemming population produces stable population cycles that repeat like clockwork.

When the lemming population becomes too great for the available food supply, large groups migrate out of the overpopulated area. Lemmings can swim and will sometimes cross water in search of a new habitat. If a large migrating group reaches a cliff overlooking water, some may jump in (or be pushed over the edge by more lemmings arriving at the rear) and start swimming; a few may die from exhaustion. This is not mass suicide but the result of the rodents following a strong migratory instinct.

JUMPING OUT OF TROUBLE In a wintry North American forest, a bobcat ambushes a snowshoe hare – a species that, like lemmings, goes through regular and highly predictable population booms and crashes.

The snowshoe hare – a North American hare whose fur turns white in winter – goes through similar population surges and crashes, in a cycle that repeats every 8 to 11 years. During a boom, the population may reach a density of 4000 hares per km^2, but during a crash it can fall to less than one hare per km^2. The hare's main predators include lynx, bobcats, great horned owls, goshawks, red fox and golden eagles, and the numbers of these species fluctuate to match that of the hares.

THE TRUTH ABOUT LEMMINGS

SNOWY OWL One of the principal predators of lemmings is the snowy owl. Here a large adult owl brings a recently killed lemming to its chicks.

LET IT RAIN

FOR SOME ANIMALS, REPRODUCTIVE OPPORTUNITIES DEPEND ON THE WEATHER AND, IN PARTICULAR, ON HEAVY RAIN. During times of drought, these creatures disappear for years at a time, but when rain arrives, they launch into a brief period of activity.

In the Australian outback is a vast, arid region known as the Lake Eyre Basin. It covers parts of Queensland, South Australia and the Northern Territory, and its focal point is Lake Eyre. On the rare occasions that it fills with water, it is the largest lake in Australia with a maximum area of about 9500 km², but for much of the time most of the lakebed is dry and covered in a salt crust that can be 50 cm thick in places. During dry periods, one of the few creatures to be seen out and about is a small, salt-adapted lizard known as the Lake Eyre dragon. The dragon shelters from the Sun among cracks in the salt crust, sometimes digging deeper into the moist mud below. The lizard stays alive by feeding on tiny harvester ants that nest in the lakebed; the ants survive on a diet of wind-blown seeds and dead insects.

Flood times

The Lake Eyre Basin drains approximately one-sixth of the Australian continent. Rainfall patterns are erratic, but when rain does fall it can be extremely heavy, especially in Queensland, in the north-east. Instead of flowing to the sea, rainwater that collects here is carried inland towards the lowest point in the basin, Lake Eyre itself, along sluggish rivers and other water channels that fill intermittently. Usually, the floodwaters are absorbed into the earth and never reach Lake Eyre, but about once every two to three years, enough water falls to reach the lake and partially fill it to a depth of about 1 m. More rarely, about three or four times a century, a massive flood completely fills Lake Eyre. This occurred in 1950 and again in 1974, when the depth reached 6 m in some places. When Lake Eyre is newly flooded, the water is almost fresh, but its salinity increases as the salt crust slowly dissolves.

PARCHED TERRAIN For much of the time, salt-covered rocks litter the dry bed of large parts of Lake Eyre in Australia. Buried in the mud, dormant life forms wait for the rain.

When even part of Lake Eyre fills with water, vast numbers of small aquatic organisms begin to hatch from eggs that may have lain dormant in the dry lakebed for years, or even decades. For a few months tiny crustaceans, such as brine shrimps, copepods and water fleas, and microscopic animals known as rotifers, grow and breed in vast numbers before the water evaporates. Large clouds of salt-loving algae may form, turning the lake pink. Huge numbers of fish, including bony bream, Lake Eyre hardyhead and golden perch arrive via floodwaters from the river systems of inland Queensland and feed on the algae and crustaceans. Water-holding frogs, which can survive several years of drought by burrowing into the ground and forming cocoons around themselves, emerge to breed. Meanwhile, the Lake Eyre dragons move to the lake's sandy shores, where they dig extensive burrows.

Bird life

The presence of a substantial amount of water in Lake Eyre attracts millions of water birds, which flock to its shores to feed on the array of fish, frogs, crustaceans, lizards and other salt-tolerant organisms that appear, and to breed and raise their young. Australian pelicans, silver gulls, banded stilts, dotterels, terns, cormorants, little grebes, ducks and red-necked stint stay as long as food is available. Eventually, the salinity increases to intolerable levels as the lake shrinks, and the fish and other creatures die in vast numbers. The birds then disperse and the lake returns to its inhospitable state, with just the harvester ants and Lake Eyre dragons scuttling over the salty surface.

SPRINGING INTO LIFE As Lake Eyre fills with water, huge numbers of brine shrimps hatch from eggs buried in the lakebed. The shrimps grow to a length of about 1 cm and have a lifespan of several months (left).

FISHING SEASON Following larger floods, pelicans are among the most noticeable of the temporary visitors at Lake Eyre. They feed in teams, corralling fish in the shallows and simultaneously dipping their bills into the water to catch them.

INDEX

PICTURE CREDITS

NATURE'S MIGHTY POWERS: POWER IN NUMBERS was published by The Reader's Digest Association Ltd, London. It was created and produced for Reader's Digest by Toucan Books Ltd, London.

The Reader's Digest Association Ltd,
11 Westferry Circus,
Canary Wharf,
London E14 4HE
www.readersdigest.co.uk

Copyright © 2009 The Reader's Digest Association Ltd

Written by
Robert Dinwiddie and Celia Coyne

FOR TOUCAN BOOKS
Editors Jane Chapman, Helen Douglas-Cooper, Andrew Kerr-Jarrett
Designers Bradbury & Williams
Picture researchers Angela Anderson, Jane Lambert, Sharon Southren, Mia Stewart-Wilson, Christine Vincent
Proofreader Marion Dent
Indexer Michael Dent

FOR READER'S DIGEST
Project editor Christine Noble
Art editor Julie Bennett
Pre-press account manager Dean Russell
Product production manager Claudette Bramble
Production controller Katherine Bunn

READER'S DIGEST, GENERAL BOOKS
Editorial director Julian Browne
Art director Anne-Marie Bulat

Colour origination Colour Systems Ltd, London
Printed and bound in China

We are committed to both the quality of our products and the service we provide to our customers. We value your comments, so please feel free to contact us on 08705 113366 or via our website at **www.readersdigest.co.uk**

If you have any comments or suggestions about the content of our books, you can email us at **gbeditorial@readersdigest.co.uk**

CONCEPT CODE: UK0138/G/S
BOOK CODE: 636-014 UP0000-1
ISBN: 978-0-276-44331-2
ORACLE CODE: 356500010H.00.24